Write A Winning
Research Proposal

How to Generate Grant Ideas and Secure
Funding Using Research Project Canvas

Martins Zaumanis

Peer Recognized series book 5

Drawings: Martins Zaumanis

Cover design: Martins Zaumanis and Jānis Eriņš

ISBN-13: 978-3-907363-19-5

1st Edition

Independently Published by Peer in 2023

Visit the *Peer Recognized* website for other books of the series:
https://peerrecognized.com

Contents

Part I: Research Project Canvas

In Part I you will see how using my **Research Project Canvas** will help you convert your research ideas into a grant proposal. With a pre-filled Project Canvas in hand, the task of writing the proposal will not seem quite so intimidating since **you will know exactly what to write within each section of your funding proposal.**

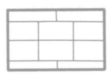

Writing Toolkit

This isn't just a book. It's a proposal writing toolkit. On the accompanying website you will access **proposal writing resources** such as *the Research Project Canvas, the Key Sentence Structure, the Background Card, the Research Idea Generator, the Proposal Writing Template, the Writing Workflow Planner, the Review Checklist, the Proposal Pitch Formula, the Graphic Design cheat sheet*, a *budget spreadsheet*, example proposals, and many useful templates.

Part II: Write Your Proposal

In Part II you will see how to write the proposal in a way that **excites and convinces any reviewer.** You will learn how to come up

with Key Sentences, then expand upon them using Story Structure. You will see how to create convincing figures, improve readability, prepare supplementary documents, and learn a formula for pitching your proposal.

Part III: Generate Ideas

In Part III of this book you will learn how to help **generate research ideas** by implementing two elements: the systematic acquisition of new knowledge and the cultivation of a creative environment. You will also learn how to strategically **select the best ideas** for your grant proposals through the delicate balancing of your creative desires with the chances of successful funding.

If you are...

☐ A young scientist preparing to write your first research proposal

☐ An experienced scientist looking to improve your chances of acquiring funding

☐ A graduate student applying for a fellowship

☐ An academic writing a research plan to apply for a promotion

... and you've been...

Overwhelmed by the task of writing a convincing proposal

Struggling to come up with research ideas

Annoyed by unproductive meetings and uncoordinated coauthors

Worried about whether you will be able to deliver on the promises of a research proposal

...then this book is for you.

Write a Winning Research Proposal will help you...

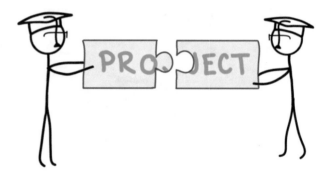

Generate research ideas

Build an environment that stimulates ideation. Once ideas start flowing, select those with the greatest potential to get funded, advance science, have an impact on society, and help advance your career.

Collaborate with co-authors

Find the right partners and make sure everyone shares the same research vision. Then divide tasks to write the proposal as efficiently as possible.

Write a clear and powerful research proposal

Use the provided tools which include the Research Project Canvas, Proposal Story Structure, Budget spreadsheet, Background Card, Proposal Scorecard, and Review Checklist to ensure that reviewers fully appreciate the value of your research idea.

Get your research proposal funded!

Why should you trust me

I wrote my first research proposal when I was a Master's student. No one had ever shown me how to write a proposal, no one was helping me and yet, amazingly, it was approved. Admittedly, at the time I did not fully appreciate the magnitude of this achievement. I thought that this is how it is supposed to be: someone has a good idea, writes a proposal and receives funding to perform the research.

In reality, though, in any given research call, only a small fraction of proposals are approved no matter how good the ideas are. It is even rarer that the very first proposal of a student is approved. So, admittedly, I was lucky.

This stroke of good luck gave me the confidence to continue writing proposals. Next, I applied for a Fulbright scholarship to study in the United States for one year. Once there, I wrote a proposal for a grant to fund my full PhD research. Later on, while I was still a Ph.D. student, I wrote a proposal to fund my postdoctoral research in Switzerland. I have written a couple of proposals per year for the past eight years since then.

My working-class family could never have afforded to pay for the years of education needed to become a scientist. Without the funding from research projects, I would have had to abandon my academic career.

Of course, writing proposals is not always ROYGBIV arcs and Rhopalocera (read: *rainbows and butterflies*). Some of my projects were rejected for not being sufficiently ambitious, others were for flying too high. A few of my proposals were, in hindsight, poorly written and frankly did not deserve to be funded. Now that I am tasked with reviewing research proposals myself, I can clearly recognize the flaws that my early proposals had.

Though being the first person with a graduate degree from my family motivated me to keep improving my proposal writing skills, I was still unsure about my chances of making it as a scientist. In a twist of fate, these insecurities turned out to be one of the cornerstones of becoming a researcher.

Had things not worked out, my Plan B involved a career in business. For even though science and business may seem quite distant occupations, I found my experience in business extremely valuable for writing research proposals. Just as entrepreneurs have to convince funders with elaborate business plans and sales pitches, scientists have to persuade grant proposal reviewers using project applications and presentations.

To learn about the business side of things, I took entrepreneurship courses and joined a business accelerator. I learned to write business plans and funding proposals for commercializing various technologies. I even had an opportunity to pitch my ideas to angel investors and clients. This experience became a cornerstone which allowed me to develop a research proposal writing approach that is far more effective than what I have seen anywhere else.

Now, a full twelve years after that first lucky proposal acceptance, after managing research projects in four different countries and receiving research grant funding in excess of $8 million, I feel confident enough to make my proposal writing approach known to other researchers. Not only do I think it will help you to improve your chances of obtaining research funding, I truly believe that my unique system will allow fellow scientists to come up with new research ideas, increase the chances of successful project execution, and ultimately make a tangible real-world impact.

*In today's competitive environment, scientists don't have the luxury of being snobbish. That's one reason why I have shamelessly borrowed the best approaches from the business world for presenting one's ideas in order to **sell my own research ideas** to reviewers, grant agencies and stakeholders.*

INTRODUCTION

RESEARCH FUNDING MAP

THE MONSTER OF
BORING IDEAS

OVERAMBITION
TEMPLE

SEA OF
REJECTED PROPOSALS

O nce upon a time, word got out that research funding was up for grabs. Crowds of money-seeking scientists rushed to collect it, but oh, how wrong they were by imagining that they could come unprepared.

The most unfit funding seekers were quickly and ruthlessly devoured by the Monster of Boring Ideas. The ones who actually started the journey had to first find their way through the thick Forest of Jargon, pass the Rocky Hills of Supervisor Comments, and cross the Bridge of Hope over the infamous Plagiarism Gorge.

Some scientists got burned by an Eruption of Co-authors, while some got sucked into the thick Literature Review Swamp. Yet other money seekers could not find their way over or around the steep Mountain of Grammatical Mistakes or avoid the incredibly tempting Siren of Procrastination.

A few brave souls who managed to overcome all of these challenges also stopped at the Church of Luck to pray to the mighty Review Gods for good fortune before taking the toughest test of them all - breaching the Fortress of Reviewers.

Any maps used for navigating the challenging road to the Treasures of Research Funding are kept secret by those who have survived the journey.

Until now that is. I wrote this book to prepare you for the adventure. So let's get started.

Funding Types for Researchers

Research project funding

These are grants to fund working on a particular research idea for a certain period of time. Such grants might be available for scientists at a specific stage of their careers. Depending on the funder, the grant themes can be defined by the funder (top-down projects) or driven by the applicant (bottom-up projects). In some cases, the objective can also be defined (e.g. the commercialization of project result, or reaching a certain technology readiness level).

Career development grants

These are scholarships that are awarded to a researcher to advance their career, or support them while they are studying. A research idea will be a part of such a proposal but the emphasis is on the person and their career plans. Often such grants are aimed at early-stage researchers, but career grants for established scientists exist as well. Grants for professional development, training, and sabbaticals also fall into this category.

Proof of concept grants

These are grants for the validation of new or ambitious ideas, or to help prepare for a larger proposal. They are typically awarded for short periods of time and entail a relatively small amount of funding. Proving the potential of an idea through such grants can increase your chances of obtaining a full research project grant.

Networking and communication

Such grants are intended for collaboration between universities and across countries. Depending on the call, they can be used for organizing conferences, establishing training networks, performing scientific outreach (communication with and educating society), enabling research stays at other institutions, and for funding attendance at conferences.

Infrastructure

These include grants for purchase of research equipment, for construction of demonstrators, for access to a specific scientific instrument, for outsourced research services, for chemicals, and consumables.

Research programs

Such grants are for high-level strategic initiatives that set research directions or manage a portfolio of projects. Examples include centers of competence or excellence or the establishment of new research centers.

The strategies presented in this book will help you when applying to any of these grant types.

Getting funded

What the reviewers expect from you

Regardless of the funding type, a project proposal needs to convince the reviewers of three things:

1. You will devote yourself to doing important work.
2. You have developed an appropriate methodology to perform it.
3. You or your team are the right persons to tackle the project.

If your proposals keep getting rejected, you should stop blaming the shortsightedness of the funding agencies, or bad luck. Either people are not interested enough in the topic, the research idea is not convincing, or you don't have the right credentials yet. In any case, you have to rethink your approach. This book will help you with this task. **In Part I you will learn what to write, in Part II how to write it, and in Part III, how to generate grant -worthy research ideas.**

What funding means for a scientist

The rewards for mastering grant writing skills are great. A successful project application will help you establish your academic independence. It will allow you to pursue areas of research that interest you, hire assistants, get the best equipment, have enough meaningful results to write impactful publications, attend conferences to meet with your peers, and collectively generate ever more ideas for new project proposals.

In other words, research funding will allow you to become peer-recognized (which *coincidentally* is the name of this book series). Peer recognition is one of the most valuable assets a scientist can have since it often snowballs into many different opportunities for doing further research.

Finally, for better or worse, many universities are now being run similar to business ventures. If you are skilled enough to be consistently able to find someone who is willing to pay for your research ideas, it serves as a third-party stamp of your value as a researcher and raises your net worth in the job market.

Only about a quarter of the US National Science Foundation (NSF) proposals get funded*. For the primary European Union research funding body, Horizon, your application has to be better than nine other proposals to receive support**.

*The National Science Foundation: An Overview. 2021, *Congressional Research Service*
**Wanzenböck et.al, Proposal success in Horizon 2020: A study of the influence of consortium characteristics. 2020, *Quant. sci. stud.*

RESEARCH PROJECT CANVAS

A scientist is staring at the blinking cursor on a computer screen, thinking of the profound magnitude of the task ahead of him - he needs to write a research proposal. He freezes.

Not only does he have to come up with a research idea with the potential to have a lasting impact in his field; he also needs to develop methodology, ensure the necessary resources and expertise are available, negotiate with prospective research partners, all while keeping the requirements of the funder in mind. Then he has to explain the whole thing in a way that will convince the reviewers that his idea is better than any of the other great research proposals that they will read.

This person used to be me. In fact, I can guarantee that almost every scientist on the planet seeking funding has felt this way.

What usually happens after this worrisome lull is that the looming deadline leaves us with no choice but to dive into the writing. The chaos that follows involves scrambling for ideas, guessing at the costs, dumping some figures into a wall of text; then rewriting everything once you find that the co-authors don't like it. This misery usually ends with an all-nighter and a submission five minutes before the deadline. It is a formidable accomplishment if the correct file gets uploaded.

In an infomercial, a grim person would say:

There has to be a better way

Just think about it. When preparing a grant application, you have the freedom to plan your own work, dream of the accomplishments that lie ahead, and imagine how they will change the world. So why is reality so different from one's aspirations?

The Research Project Canvas

The *Research Project Canvas* is the centerpiece of this book. I created the one-page Project Canvas template as the missing intermediate step that allows grant seekers to efficiently turn their ideas into a finished proposal.

Filling the Project Canvas

The Project Canvas will help you to plan and outline your proposal, collaborate with co-authors, improve the proposal's chances of success, generate ideas and rate their potential.

OUTLINING ———

BRAINSTORMING ———

COLLABORATING ———

IMPROVING ———

GENERATING IDEAS ———

RATING IDEAS ★★★☆☆ ———

Birth of the Research Project Canvas

I was inspired to create the *Research Project Canvas* technique after reading the *Business Model Generation**. Described in the book, the *Business Model Canvas* provides a way to swiftly explore different business ideas and decide which ones to follow through with. The *Business Model Canvas* also serves as a means for communicating with business advisors, and it helps with writing a full-fledged business plan.

I felt that this concept was similar to scientists validating research ideas, negotiating with partners and writing a research project proposal, so I developed a canvas that would apply to the scientific field.

The filled Project Canvas

Once filled, the Project Canvas will allow you to convincingly describe each scientific part of your proposal.

Use of the filled Project Canvas

The Project Canvas will also enable you to efficiently use the supplementary tools and techniques in this book.

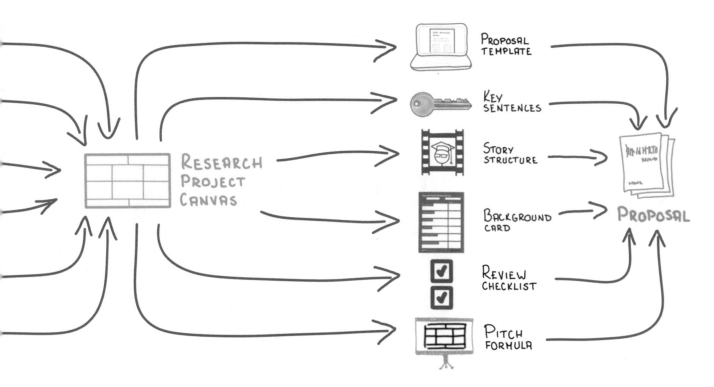

*Osterwalder, et al. Business Model Generation: A Handbook For Visionaries, Game Changers, and Challengers. *2010, John Wiley & Sons.*

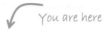
The 10 Building Blocks of a

The one-page Research Project Canvas template consists of ten building blocks that make up the key elements of any research proposal. Each block provides questions that will help you to fill in the template.

On the following pages you will learn how to fill the canvas and discover what project reviewers expect to see in each section of a successful proposal.

1 Problem

The knowledge gap that should be filled

2 Objectives

The objectives that will help solve the identified problem

3 Methodology

The approach that leads to reaching the objectives

4 Resources

The resources needed to accomplish the objectives

5 Participants

The team's qualification for implementing the methodology and their complementary value

6 Results and Impact

The new knowledge that will be created and its real-world impact

7 Dissemination

The proper target audience and how to reach them

8 Timeline

The time required for performing each part of the project

9 Budget

The major cost items and the distribution of funding between participants

10 Funder's Requirements

The rules that govern the project's contents

Research Project Canvas

You can access the **Research Project Canvas template** in PDF, PowerPoint, and in the form of an online whiteboard at: https://peerrecognized.com/projectcanvas

Research Project Canvas	Project title:	Designed by:	Date:

Problem ❓	Objectives ◎	
Results and Impact 📈	**Participants** 👥	**Methodology** ⬚
Dissemination 📋	**Timeline** 📅	**Resources** ⚙
Funder's requirements ☑☑	**Budget** $	

Created by: **Martins Zaumanis**

Peer Recognized
www.peerrecognized.com

1 Problem

Summarize in the Problem block a real-world pain that needs to be solved. Once established, specify the knowledge gap that you will fill with your research.

What real-world problem are we solving?
Why should the problem be solved?
What is the specific knowledge gap that we will fill?

Example problem
Preventing the spread of malaria

Example research gap:
Is the vaccine XYZ safe for adolescents seeking to create immunity against malaria?

How to describe the problem within the proposal

Relevant proposal sections:
Introduction / Background / Literature review / Prior research / Significance

Problem definition

The state-of-the-art (or background) section of a proposal should first provide enough evidence to make it absolutely clear to the reviewers that there is a real-world problem that needs to be solved. After all - it does not matter how great your research plan is if you are addressing a problem that is not worth solving. In other words - a reviewer who is not convinced about the seriousness of the problem might make an irrevocable decision to decline the proposal even before reading what its objectives are.

Background

The background section should place the planned research in the context of what has already been achieved. Do this by citing literature, providing statistics, informing about case studies, and by presenting your preliminary or ongoing studies. Rather than simply citing the literature, perform critical analysis, comment on larger trends in the field, and don't shy away from sources that contradict your approach.

Knowledge gap

Funding agencies often struggle to find enough experts on a particular topic. This means that the people reading your proposal might have a significantly different background than you do. Failing to take a step back and properly introduce the problem might make the reviewer question the necessity of performing the research in the first place.

This analysis of the real-world problem should provide the groundwork for introducing the specific knowledge gap (or gaps) that you plan to address in the project. You must demonstrate how your work will build on what has already been done, before proposing something innovative or unique about your planned research.

Your own background

A thorough analysis of the literature should serve to demonstrate your proficiency regarding the proposed research topic, but you can make the case even more compelling by describing your own prior research relates to the direction of the proposed research. For career grants, you can even mention your personal motivation to address the problem. All of this should convince the reviewer that you are literate in the respective science field and have enough insight and the desire to make a valuable contribution.

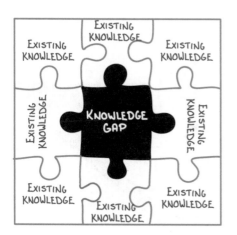

It isn't enough to simply identify a knowledge gap. You also should answer the "So what?" question by demonstrating why it is important to close it.

23

2 Objectives

The Objectives block is where you specify your goal for solving the specific knowledge gap that you identified in the Problem block.

What main objective will move us toward solving the identified problem?
What are the specific sub-objectives of the project?

Objective formulation
Phrase the overall objective in one sentence.
Add more specific sub-objectives for different parts of the project

How to describe objectives within the proposal

Following the **SMART** criteria* process will help you to develop the objectives.

Specific

Express the main objective succinctly in order to make it absolutely clear to the reviewers what it is that you want to achieve within the project.

Most proposals will have multiple sub-projects. You might want to state a specific objective for each of them.

Organizing your objectives using bullet points will help maintain brevity and hierarchy.

If possible, organize any sub-objectives in a logical order (i.e. each building on the previous one), or based on the duration it will take to achieve them.

Measurable

Ideally the objectives should be unambiguously testable. Phrasing them in the form of a hypothesis is one way of ensuring this. A clear statement of what will be accomplished, and even providing criteria against which the objectives can be tested, is another good approach.

Ambitious

It's tough to find a balance between having overly and insufficiently ambitious objectives for a proposal. The sweet spot will depend on your seniority, expectations of the funder, and the likelihood of achieving the results.

We will come back to gauging your ambitions in Part III of this book.

Realistic

For each objective ask yourself: Is this reasonably likely to be achieved within the current technological and conceptual constraints? You should also make sure that the resources that you are requesting are enough to reach the objective.

Time-related

Can you realistically expect to reach each objective within the time-frame available for the project?

*The original SMART criteria, coined by George T.Doran, includes of Smart, Measurable, Assignable, Realistic, and Time-related parts

3 Methodology

Use the Methodology block to define the major steps for how you plan to reach your objective. You might include the main methods, key variables, and the means for data analysis. Large projects should be divided into smaller units, such as work packages and specific tasks. Sketching the methodology as a diagram is a great way to fill out this block

What methodology will allow us to reach our objective?
What is the research hypothesis?
What methods should we employ and what data should we collect?
How should we divide the work into smaller units (work packages, tasks)?
How are the different parts interconnected?

Methodology basics
Population
Sample size
Variables
Employed methods
Type of analysis
Work packages
Tasks
Deliverables
Milestones

How to describe methodology within the proposal

Relevant proposal sections:
Methodology / Research approach / Work plan / Methods / Activities / Tasks / Research design

Research methodology is quite obviously one of the most important aspects of a research proposal. You have to convince the reviewers that the approach you've selected is appropriate for achieving the objectives and delivering the promised results within the given time period of the project.

The scientific method

Use the scientific method (see next page) as the basis and build up from there. Describe the research design, the variables you will include, the population you will study, the sample size, the data collection means, and the methods you will employ to analyze the gathered information.

In some fields, ethics principles have to be described in detail as well.

Stay focused

Be specific in describing the methodology. For example, include a brief description of the experimental methods you will rely upon, add a summary of the materials that you are going to use, attach samples of questionnaires that you will use, and include any other proof that demonstrates the thoroughness you have put into developing the research plan.

Adding a flowchart is a great way to present the methodology. In Part II you will see how to develop one.

While details increase credibility, you should still keep your writing concise and focus on the most important elements. Reviewers hate superfluous information. In a pro-

posal, you don't need to include as much detail as is used in a methodology section of a research paper.

Justify your approach

Besides describing the methodology, justify why you selected it over other approaches that could have been used to reach the same objectives.

At the same time, be realistic and acknowledge that your proposed approach might not work out. One-trick ponies rarely get very far. The reviewers need to know that the research will not stop if, after a couple of months, the initial approach fails to bear results. So indicate alternative methods for tackling the identified problem (this is often done using a risk analysis table).

Work packages are usually the largest units of a project, each having a distinct objective and research approach. Work packages can hold multiple tasks. For large projects, work packages may be grouped into modules.

Tasks are concrete steps for moving towards an objective. Tasks are often organized into concise numbered lists.

Deliverables are tangible outcomes of the project. These can be a report, method, presentation, software code, prototype, website, patent, video, diagram, dataset, and the like.

Milestones are checkpoints that mark important steps toward reaching the project's objectives. They can delineate, for example, the decisions that will affect the future course of the project.

To describe methodology, a specific jargon is often used for defining the smaller units of the project.

This book will help you write a research proposal; it is not intended to teach you all there is to know about experimental design. However, reviewing key principles of the Scientific Method will help you get going. Use these elements as a starting point and then dig deeper to develop a relevant research methodology for your proposal.

Included in the Problem block of the Research Project Canvas

A research **question** is a clear and concise inquiry that defines the scope and purpose of a research study. A good research question should be relevant and help generate new knowledge to address the identified **problem**.

Background research involves literature review and the gathering of other information related to the research question. This allows researchers to understand the existing knowledge and theories which helps to ensure a solid foundation for defining a good

Hypothesis is an informed guess or prediction that is based on prior knowledge or evidence. It typically includes a statement about the relationship between two or more variables, and may include a prediction about the direction and strength of the relationship. Importantly, it should be phrased in a way that allows you to

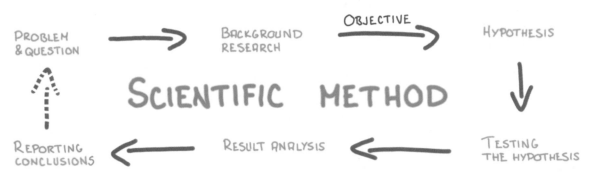

Reporting conclusions allows other scientists and the wider community to learn from, validate, and build upon the new knowledge. This often leads to new questions that require to re-apply the scientific method.

Research results are typically published through peer-reviewed scientific papers. To learn the **LEAP method** for writing research papers, read

Result analysis allows concluding whether the collected data supports or rejects the hypothesis. The process involves interpreting the results, looking for correlations between variables, performing statistical analysis, and comparing the results with existing literature and theories.

Testing the hypothesis involves conducting experiments or performing observational studies that allow you to verify or negate the hypothesis. The testing method should be selected in a way that enables a statistically valid analysis and limits the possibility that the results occur by chance or that they can be explained by an alterna-

Key Elements of the Scientific Method

Research Design

Common **research designs** include experiments, surveys, case studies, and observational studies. The choice of research design will depend on factors such as the nature of your research question, the type of data you wish to collect, and the available resources.

Variables

A variable is any factor or condition that can be manipulated, controlled, or measured. Careful selection of variables enables scientists to test hypotheses, establish cause-and-effect relationships, and draw reliable conclusions.

Independent variables are the factors that researchers change in order to observe their effects on other variables. For example, in a study on the effects of exercise on weight loss, the independent variable would be the amount of exercise the participants engage in.

Dependent variables are the factors that are measured or observed in response to the independent variable. In the weight loss study, the dependent variable would be the participant's weight loss.

Control variables are factors that are held constant to isolate the effects of the independent variable.

Extraneous variables are factors that could potentially affect the dependent variable but are not being studied.

Boundary conditions refer to the constraints or limitations that are imposed on a study by its context, setting, or methodology. They allow defining the scope and limitations of their study, and to identify the factors that may affect the generalizability of their findings.

Sampling

Population refers to the entire group of individuals, objects, or phenomena that a researcher is interested in studying. The choice of population depends on the research question and the scope of the study.

Sample refers to a subset of the population that is selected for the study. A representative sample enables generalizing the findings to the population. Depending on the research question and the characteristics of the population, sampling can be done using various techniques, such as random sampling, purposive sampling, or stratified sampling, The size of the sample is also important as it impacts the precision and accuracy of the results.

Data collection and analysis

Data collection involves gathering data through various methods such as surveys, interviews, observation, or experiments. Choose the data collection methods that can verify your hypothesis, and are valid, reliable, and ethical.

Data analysis methods will depend on the nature of your research question and the type of data you collect. Common data analysis methods include statistical analysis, content analysis, and thematic analysis. An appropriate data analysis can identify patterns, trends, and relationships, and to draw conclusions.

Data management describes how you will collect, preserve and share research data. Some funders require this in the proposal, but even if not required, sharing data helps to ensure reproducibility and generate trust.

Ethics

Ethical principles in ensure that research is conducted in a trustworthy manner, and that the rights and welfare of participants are protected. The types of issues that should be considered in the proposal include confidentiality of sensitive data, minimizing any harm to participants and the environment, and ensuring the consent of participants.

The researchers themselves must also comply with ethical standards, including avoiding potential conflicts of interest or biases, as well as ensuring honesty and integrity.

4 Resources

In the Resources block, include the key resources necessary to complete the project, including required equipment, key partnerships, important know-how, available data, materials, co-funding and anything else needed to implement the methodology. Consider this block a reality check to determine whether you have everything you need to successfully execute the project.

What key resources does the methodology require?
How do we access the required resources?

Types of resources
Crucial equipment/infrastructure
Prior know-how
Key partners
Materials
Data
Patents
Co-funding

How to describe resources within the proposal

Available equipment

Proposal reviewers need to be certain that you have access to all the necessary resources for implementing your stated methodology. To ensure that they are convinced, you need to describe the key research facilities, infrastructure and available testing equipment. If the funder has any doubts about the capabilities of your laboratory, you could include a table with the key equipment and a short description of what you will use it for.

If relevant, describe where you will obtain any required materials, reagents or chemicals.

If you don't possess the essential resources, describe how you will access them. The outsourcing of testing, and purchase or rental of equipment from the grant funds are some options.

Include non-physical resources

Don't forget that resources include more than just equipment. Prior know-how, patents, available data, key partners, readily available co-funding and even moral support from stakeholders can be valuable resources. Adding such details with descriptions will increase credibility. For example, include links to relevant data, any prior research, attach support letters, and add whatever else you feel might strengthen your claims.

Sprinkle resources throughout the proposal

Proposal templates often do not have a dedicated section for describing resources. Therefore, you may need to incorporate such information throughout relevant sections of the proposal such as methodology, description of the research team, available co-funding and dissemination partners.

Add relevant links

Proposals typically have a strict page limit which may not allow you to include everything that the reviewer might want to see. Unless the submission guide prohibits it, a clever way to circumvent this is to include a hyperlink to websites that provide such information. For example, you might include a link to the laboratory website which provides a thorough description of the equipment you have access to.

Caution: Don't assume that the reviewer will click links. Be sure to include all essential information in the proposal itself. Links should only be used for supplementary, less crucial, data.

5 Participants

The Participants block is where you demonstrate that you (or your team) have the right skills to complete the project.
You can mention accomplishments that relate to the project and define how participant's skill-sets will complement each other.

Which key participants will allow us to reach the objective?
What are the strengths of each participant?
What is each partner going to do?
How will partners complement each other?

Key accomplishments
Related publications
Previous teamwork
Consortium strengths
Role of each participant
Noteworthy related results

How to describe participants within the proposal

Relevant proposal sections:
Applicants / Research team / Synergies / Principal Investigators

Show subject-matter expertise

You have to convince the reviewers that you or your research team can be reasonably expected to reach the proposed objectives and deliver the promised results. To do this, be sure to present the work that the participants have already undertaken on the topic and describe its relevance to the current proposal.

Mentioning any preliminary results will help bolster your case by showing the reviewers that you are already invested in the subject.

Adding a brief description of the institutions where they work might add further credibility. It will show that the individuals participating in the proposal have the necessary support.

Highlight large accomplishments

Describe the qualifications that make the research team suitable for the project. This is not the time to be self-conscious about your accomplishments. Stay professional and use facts to state your claims, but seek to prove that you have assembled the dream team for this research project.

Describe teamwork synergy

If more than one person is applying for the project, describe how the competencies of each team member complement each other.

If they exist, show any previous collaborations between team members (e.g. joint projects, co-authored papers, research visits) since this can reassure the reviewers that the proposed team is compatible.

Remember to note what role each key researcher will have in the proposed project.

Ideas for what to mention in the proposal

- Related research projects that you have worked on
- Previous collaborations between participants
- Relevant peer-reviewed publications, books, monographs
- Prior results to use in project, like code, datasets, prototypes and patents
- Related awards, honors and fellowships
- Supervision and teaching of students on the subject
- Outreach and knowledge transfer activities in the area of proposal, like public engagement, appearances in media, etc

 This is not to say that you should duplicate the researchers' CV in the proposal text. Rather, just pick the key accomplishments that demonstrate the competence of the researcher as it relates to the proposal.

6 Results and Impact

The Results and Impact block is where you list the new knowledge that will be created and the impact that the results will have towards solving the identified real-world problem. You can also specify which groups will be impacted most by the results.

What new knowledge will be generated?
How will the project impact your field and beyond?
Who benefits and in what way ?
(researchers, policymakers, education, industry, society, economy)

Typical results
New methods
New/improved procedures
Code
Models
New knowledge

Possible impacts
Competitive advantage
Environmental or social benefits
Change in values, beliefs, attitude
Increased awareness
Better education
Economic gains
Policy change

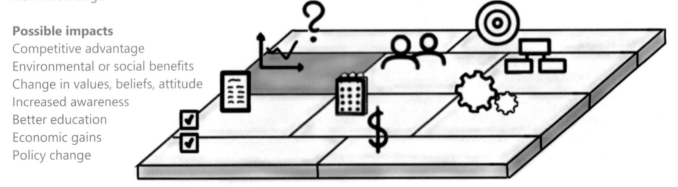

How to describe results and impact within the proposal

Generated knowledge

You can not know exactly what the results of a research project will be. Trying to solve the puzzle that you have identified (for which you might or might not have all the pieces) is the whole point of doing research.

However, you should know exactly what new knowledge you are going to generate. In other words, while you can not know if you will make a significant contribution toward solving the identified problem, you should certainly know which meaningful results the project will generate to fill the identified knowledge gap one way or another.

Put results in context

Be sure to mention the core results that you expect from the project, be it a better understanding of a partic-

ular subject, a new method, or any other specific result the project will deliver. Ideally, you should demonstrate how the findings will be applicable to contexts other than the narrow boundaries of your research study.

Impact

The proposal should also clearly demonstrate the impact that the results will have in your scientific field and beyond. Remember to explain exactly how the ambition of the project goes beyond the state of the art that you covered in the background description.

Describing the potential impacts is especially important if you are planning an applied research project or performing experimental development. If that is the case, be sure to mention what innovations and im-

provements can be expected and how the practitioners will be able to use them. If the results of an applied research project will not be ready for practical implementation right after your project is over, indicate how and in what timeframe they will.

Every project has an impact

When describing the impact of a fundamental research project, highlight the ways in which other researchers could benefit from them. If you plan to use the results for future research, teaching, or as a basis for a follow-up research project, mention this as well.

Outline the next steps

Funding agencies don't want to suspect that projects will simply fall off a cliff once the funding runs out. You might want to include a few sentences about an expected follow-up project, continued dissemination, use in teaching, spinoffs, patents, transfer to the industry and, in some cases, even whether an impact on the economy or job creation is expected.

Do your homework

Regardless of whether you are looking for funding from a science foundation, a government agency, or a private company, you can be sure they have their own goals when handing out funding. Do your research on the website of the funder to find out what their mission is and show in the proposal how your research will have a positive impact on their mission.

7 Dissemination

Describe in the Dissemination block how you will deliver the generated results to the target audience. Be specific and note how many papers you will write, at which conferences you will give presentations, and how you will make the data, code, and other information from the Results block available to the people who need to see it. Protecting intellectual property is one part of the dissemination strategy.

Who is the target audience?
How do we reach them?
Who and how will exploit the results?
What knowledge can be shared?
What IP has to be protected?

Typical dissemination channels
Scientific journals
Conference presentations
Data repositories
The Internet
Workshops/meetings/webinars
Apps/prototypes
Patents
Training
Traditional media

How to describe dissemination within the proposal

Relevant proposal sections:
Dissemination / Exploitation / Communication / Outreach

A successful dissemination strategy provides an opportunity for your project results to make an impact in science and the world beyond it.

When describing dissemination approach, start off by thinking who your target audience is and work backwards to identify the best means of reaching them. For example:

Other scientists

If the target audience is other scientists, you will be best off publishing the results in research journals and scientific conferences. For larger projects you might consider organizing a workshop or a symposium.

Industry stakeholders

If your audience is industry professionals, consider publishing your study results in industry magazines, presenting them at industry conferences, contributing to standards, preparing leaflets and manuals as well as contacting professional associations. In a larger project you might develop a demonstrator, an app or a prototype that you reveal during a special event.

Society

If your audience is the general society, think of ways to appear in mainstream newspapers, websites and television. Not only this will help to share the results; it might create some buzz about you and your research.

Internet target groups

Of course, the Internet can be used to reach any target groups. You can set up a website, post in social media groups, organize communities, create online presentations, facilitate webinars, and publish videos.

Funder's desires

A project's dissemination strategy will depend not only on your personal skills and preferences, but also on the expectations of the project funder and partners.

Most public funding agencies expect wide dissemination of the project results. Companies, on the other hand, may want to keep certain aspects of the know-how for themselves as a proprietary advantage. But even industry partners usually appreciate the positive exposure that a research project can bring. Presentations at conferences, an article in an industry magazine, a press release, and sharing on social media will probably sound appealing for a company.

Open access benefits

After exploiting opportunities arising from the research result, and making sure any intellectual property is protected, consider making the research data accessible to anyone. Published research data not only holds immense potential for the advancement of science; it can be very beneficial for you as a researcher as well. It will increase your credibility, you will likely gather more citations, and you will increase the chances that the results are actually used. Funders, especially public agencies, often look favorably on a proposal to openly share data (some agencies even require it). You can access further information about open data sharing at https://peerrecognized.com/projectcanvas

Three broad groups for describing activities related to result sharing

1   **Communication** generates awareness about the project among stakeholders and informs society about the progress of your research (and the spending of public money, if used).

2   **Dissemination** of your work to others with the goal of advancing the scientific field and allow other researchers to learn from your results and build upon them.

3   **Exploitation** is the adaptation of your research results such that they are incorporated into standards, guidelines, laws, commercialization of products, or use in fulfilling societal needs. This often takes place at the final phase, or after the project is over. Communication and Dissemination can certainly facilitate exploitation but you should include additional activities specifically aimed at increasing the chances of successful exploitation.

Here are a few different ways of informing the world about your research results. The borders between the activity types are somewhat arbitrary and you can feel free to move the How's around as you see fit.

	To who (audience)	How	When
Communication	- General public - Media - Stakeholders	- Press releases - Traditional media - Social media - Infographics - Website - Video - Exhibitions	Throughout the project
Dissemination	- Other scientists - Authorities - Industry - Policymakers - Associations - Businesses - NGOs	- Scientific publications - Academic conferences - Data sharing - Workshops - White papers - Website - Tradeshow - Video - Leaflets - Newsletters - Influencers	As soon as there are publishable results
Exploitation		- Prototypes/demonstrators - SWOT analysis - Business models/ plans - Patents/ IP management - Standardization - Adaptation for teaching - Follow-up projects - Roadmaps - Training/seminars - Apps/software - Manuals - Meetings with stakeholders	As soon as there are exploitable results (typically near the end and beyond the project)

8 Timeline

In the Timeline block you estimate how long the project will take by including a schedule of tasks and milestones for the work listed in the Methodology block. You might also want to note when the results will be disseminated and any important considerations regarding the availability of resources or brainpower. Sketching a simple Gantt chart is a good way to fill the Timeline block.

How long will the project take?
When are specific activities planned to occur?
When will we reach important milestones?
Who contributes what and when?
When does travel take place?

Typical items of a Gantt Chart
Work packages
Tasks
Milestones
Deliverables
Interdependency
Travel

How to describe the timeline within the proposal

Relevant proposal sections:
Time plan / Calendar graphic / Gantt chart

Break down the steps

A project time plan lets you break the proposal into smaller, identifiable steps. These steps can include Work Packages (WPs), tasks, milestones, deliverables and such. These are typically displayed using a Gantt chart which is broken down into months (quarters for longer projects).

Description

In addition to the Gantt chart, you might want to include a brief description of the rationale used for organizing the research in the presented sequence and the interdependency of different parts of the project.

Add details

Gantt charts are often underused. You can include a lot of valuable information in one. For example, you can add milestones and deliverables (refer to letters M and D in the example chart). In a similar way, you can add information regarding your dissemination activities or planned travel. You can even highlight the persons (or teams) who are responsible for each task using color coding. If a certain task can not be started before a previous one is finished, you can add arrows to demonstrate the dependency. Just don't try to jam all of this into a single graph; too much information will likely make it confusing.

Be realistic

Gantt charts, including milestones and deliverables, are often used to control the purse strings of the project by the funder. This means that if you make the calendar plan unrealistic, you risk losing your funding stream.

It is always a good idea to add a buffer of 10-20% more time to your best estimate to account for unforeseen events and delays.

Stage	2019												2020												2021											
	1	2	3	4	5	6	7	8	9	10	11	12	1	2	3	4	5	6	7	8	9	10	11	12	1	2	3	4	5	6	7	8	9	10	11	12
WP1 Management																																				
Management																																				
Steering Committee Meetings	M1																																			
WP2 RAP management																																				
RA characterisation test study											M4																									
RA processing study																							D1													
WP3 Performance-based design																																				
Mixture aging study									M3				M6																							
Balanced design study																						D3														
WP4 Long term performance																																				
Accelerated testing using MMLS3																																	M7			
Test section monitoring																																				D4
WP5 Dissemination																																				
Scientific articles, conferences,																																				
Report																																				D5

Gantt chart of one of my own research projects

9 Budget

The Budget block is where you estimate the project costs by breaking down the main expenses. For a consortium, define how the expenses will be divided between the partners.

What are the major expenses of the project?
How much will the needed resources cost?
What is the budget of each partner?

Example costs
Salaries and wages
New equipment
Infrastructure use
Project management
Intellectual property
Subcontracting
Materials
Direct research costs
Consumables
Dissemination
Overheads or indirect costs

How to describe budget within the proposal

Finding a balance

The budget section is challenging to complete because you have to calculate the costs for a vaguely defined amount of work (the research process is difficult to predict) for a period that may last several years into the future. You also have to balance the budget with the expectations of the grant agency and your supervisor. In collaborative projects, each of your partners will have to go through the same procedure internally and eventually everyone will have to settle for a compromise while ensuring that the budget corresponds with the requirements of the funding agency.

Sometimes the budgeting process will require taking a step back to adjust the objectives and the amount of planned work.

Since this process can be tricky, the best advice I can give is for you to be as realistic as possible when calculating the costs because reviewers will punish proposals for either under- or over-budgeting.

Use the Project Canvas for your estimates

Start budget planning by first considering all the Research Project Canvas blocks, then make a list of all the things you have to do. See examples on the next page.

Justify the expenditures

You will be required to provide justification for each cost item. Usually, this involves answering the following two questions:

- Why is this item in the budget?
- How did you calculate the total sum?

Comply with the submission guide

The funding agency defines what costs can and can not be included. Some funders will not sponsor equipment purchases, others might not pay salaries. Others may define the minimum/maximum budget for the proposal, or require co-funding (cost-sharing) by the applicants.

In-kind contributions

In-kind contributions are non-cash resources (e.g. labor, materials, equipment) that a participant or partner contributes to a project.

Some funders require that you obtain co-funding that can be provided in the form of in-kind contributions. Some funders don't require it, but still see it as a positive, while other agencies forbid in-kind contributions from the industry altogether, afraid that it might make the researchers biased.

Costs categories

Category	Examples
Salaries and wages	Researchers, students, technicians, administrative personnel Remember to include social security contributions, benefits, insurance, vacation (calculated as a percentage of costs for wages)
New equipment	Equipment, delivery, installation, training
Infrastructure use	Space rental, amortization of equipment, computing time, data storage, disposal of hazardous waste, insurance, calibration, maintenance, energy cost
Project management	Meetings, travel, communication
Intellectual property	Data, books, patents, software
Subcontracting	Testing, services, consulting
Materials	Cost of materials and delivery
Direct research costs	Fieldwork, travel, reimbursement of research participants, costs per test
Consumables	Reagents, chemicals, laboratory expendables
Dissemination	Conferences, open-access publishing, data repositories, workshops, website, event organization, training activities
Overheads or indirect costs	Normally calculated as a percentage of the total costs according to the rules set internally or by the funding agency (used for the lab space, IT infrastructure, library, utilities, wages of the finance department, etc.)

Example costs table for a simple proposal

Item	Description	Total cost, $	Justification
Salary PI	10% FTE×2 years×$100,000/year + 15% benefits	**23,000**	Coordinate the project, analyze results, write scientific papers, report to funding agency
Salary PhD student	100% FTE×2 years×$30,000/year + 15% benefits	**69,000**	Analyze literature, perform tests, contribute to analysis
Salary technician	5% FTE×2 years×$60,000/year + 15% benefits	**6,900**	Pick up field samples, run complex tests
Equipment	Price $12,000, delivery 1,000	**13,000**	Test device X for Task 2.1 (WP2)
Materials	Company Z contributes materials worth $3000	**3,000**	In-kind contribution of additive for WP3
Dissemination	2 open-access papers ($2000 each) and 1 conference ($600 travel, $300 room&board, $600 registration)	**3,500**	1 paper on XYZ; 1 paper on ABC, 1 presentation on IJK
Overheads	25% of direct costs	**29,600**	According to the funding agency rules

Requested funding	**148,000**	
In-kind contribution	3,000	
Total project costs	145,000	

Budgeting spreadsheet

The funders often require you to fill a provided spreadsheet or a web-form. However, I usually first use my own spreadsheet to estimate the costs. It helps to break down the costs by research work packages, and individual tasks. This enables estimating costs within various budget categories (e.g. personnel costs, equipment). You can download my **budgeting spreadsheet** from www.peerrecognized.com/projectcanvas.

For a collaborative project, you could ask each partner to fill in a spreadsheet themselves and then merge everything into a single file.

Funder's Requirements

In the Funder's Requirements block, make note of the anticipated funder and define their key requirements for the project, including budget constraints, eligible costs, eligibility requirements, etc. You should also note the main criteria used for proposal evaluation.

What requirements are set by the funding body?
Expected budget? Which costs can be funded?
Key criteria for project evaluation?

Typical requirements
Research objectives
Min/max budget
Eligible costs
Employment status/seniority of researchers
Type of legal entity
Consortium size/type
Target technology readiness level

Possible funding sources
Science Foundation
Government agencies
International organizations
NGO's
Industry associations
Private companies
Foundations
Own university
Lab resources

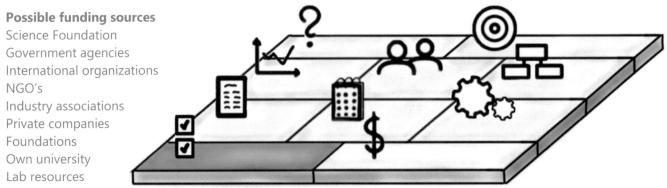

How to deal with funder's requirements in the proposal

Relevant proposal sections:
All

The holy requirements

The Funder's Requirements block is there to remind you to fulfill the wishes of the research funder. Most often the requirements will be expressed in a proposal submission guide and available for download from the website of the funding agency.

Treat the submission guide like a Monk treats the Bible and follow its strict requirements to the last detail. The funder might set requirements for the topic, your experience, employment conditions, host institution, the research team, funding amount, and so forth.

What you would like to do in the research is irrelevant unless it falls within the boundaries defined by the funder.

Do your homework

Read the guide carefully to determine whether this is the right place to submit a proposal:

- Make sure you are eligible to participate.
- Find a database of projects the funder sponsored in the past to see if their scale and ambition are in line with what you would like to propose. You can also ask for sample proposals from peers.
- Determine the success rate of previous projects to decide if the risk and required effort is worth it at this stage of your career.
- Ask your peers about the research call. People who have received funding (or even unsuccessful applicants) can usually give a lot of useful tips. You can also ask for a sample proposal.
- Attend the call information sessions organized by the agency or your university
- If something is unclear, consult your more experienced peers or ask the grant agency's program officer. Being well-informed about all the requirements will considerably increase your chances of success if

you decide to apply. We will return to this in Part II.

Check the evaluation criteria

Write down each criteria for evaluating the proposal (these are typically published in the call guidelines). Now you can rate and check off the items that you have described in the proposal.

Make reviewer's work easy

Applied research calls often contain a list of items that have to be addressed in the call. Consider including a table in the proposal summarizing how you have addressed each requirement and where in the proposal such details are provided.

Administrative details matter

My colleague's proposal was rejected because the properties of the PhD file he submitted held his name. Although this may seem a ridiculous reason to reject a proposal, the colleague could not refute the decision because it was clearly written in the research call that the metadata should be anonymized. Be sure to check the requirements and use the writing template if provided.

Research Call Scorecard

Before deciding to put the effort into writing the proposal, it's best to take a critical look at the research call. The *Research Call Scorecard* will help you to do this by highlighting all of the different considerations that might affect your decision.

Download the **Research Call Scorecard** at:
https://peerrecognized.com/projectcanvas

Research Call Scorecard

Generate ideas > **Find Funding** > Conceptualize > Write > Review > Submit

Review the research call using this scorecard before starting to write a proposal. It supplements the Research Project Canvas by M. Zaumanis.

Research call: [title]   Filled by: [name]   Date: [date]

Criteria	Negative	Score (-3 to +3)	Positive	Example questions to answer
My interest	The call topic seems boring		I would like to work on the call topic for years	Would I love working on it?
Workload for preparing a proposal	I need a lot of effort (many pages, inviting partners, additional documents, etc.)		I have the time to take this on. I have a team that will support me	Number of pages to write? My expertise in the topic? My experience with this funder?
Call requirements	It would be difficult or impossible to fulfill all the requirements		I am well positioned to accomplish everything required	Requirements for research topics, partners, consortium, co-funding, additional documents, budgeting, ...?
Success rate	Low success rate		High success-rate	What's the success rate of previous calls (ask colleagues, check website)?
My career development	The call does not fit me at this moment (too big/small, restrictive requirements, etc.)		This project would benefit my career	My future plans (research topics/ location/ institution/ family, ...)? The future prospects of the topic?
Project duration, timing	I am not able to fit this project into my schedule (conflicts with other projects, have to move soon, etc.)		I would have the time to work on such a project.	Start date, duration, completion date?
My expertise	I do not have, or cannot prove, my expertise on the topic of the call		I can present my track record on the topic.	Requirements related to experience, age, degree, track record?
Resources	It would be difficult to access or acquire everything needed for the project		I have everything readily available	What resources are required to implement the methodology? Does my institution fit the call requirements?
External motivation	I am under serious pressure to get a project		I can freely choose what to work on	What forces me to apply (in need of funding, pressure from institution, require equipment, seeking a VISA, ...?

Total score (count the points): [points]

Technology Readiness Level

A Technology Readiness Level (TRL) is a standardized framework for evaluating the maturity and progress of a technology. It was first developed by NASA, but many research agencies have since adopted it. By assigning a TRL to your research, you can communicate its readiness to industry partners. Just keep in mind that the definitions of the levels can vary slightly depending on the agency*.

EXPERIMENTAL DEVELOPMENT

PRODUCT INNOVATION

APPLIED RESEARCH

FUNDAMENTAL RESEARCH

$$F = \left(\frac{m}{t}\right)V$$

TRL 9 — Actual system proven in an operational environment

TRL 8 — System complete and qualified

TRL 7 — System prototype demonstration in an operational environment

TRL 6 — Technology demonstrated in a relevant environment

TRL 5 — Technology validated in a relevant environment

TRL 4 — Technology validated in a lab

TRL 3 — Experimental proof of concept

TRL 2 — Technology concept formulated

TRL 1 — Basic principles observed

*TRL description from BRIDGE2HE project, Guiding notes to use the TRL self-assessment tool, 2022, *Horizon Europe*

Types of Research Projects

	Fundamental research	Applied research
Definition*	Fundamental (or basic) research* is experimental or theoretical work undertaken primarily to acquire new knowledge of the underlying foundation of phenomena and observable facts, without any particular application or use in view.	Applied research* is original investigation undertaken to acquire new knowledge. It is, however, directed primarily towards a specific practical aim or objective.
Example questions	Which hypothesis about a certain phenomena is true? What theory explains this phenomena? What does this artwork indicate about society at the time?	How do we treat this disease? How can we advance this technology? How can we expand upon the results of basic research?
Example project*	Historians study the history and human impact of glacial outburst floods in a country.	Researchers study microwaves and thermal coupling with nanoparticles to properly align and sort carbon nanotubes.
Example funders	National Science Foundation National Health Agency University research funds	Government agencies (e.g. defense, health, etc.) Foundations Private companies Industry associations University research funds
Usual call types	Bottom-up	Top-down Bottom-up
Typical use of results	Scientific papers Books Scientific theories	Scientific papers Patents Products Methods Systems

*OECD Frascati Manual 2015: Guidelines for Collecting and Reporting Data on Research and Experimental Development. 2015, *OECD Publishing*

Experimental development

Experimental development* is systematic work, drawing on knowledge gained from research and practical experience and producing additional knowledge, which is focused on producing new products or processes, or to improve existing products or processes.

How to reduce costs without sacrificing performance?
How to optimize this prototype so that it meets certification requirements?
How can we adapt a new technology for this product?

The development and testing (in a classroom) of software and support tools, based on fieldwork, to improve mathematics cognition for student special education.

Private companies
Industry associations

Top-down

Products
Patents

Typical exploitation of research results

EXPERIMENTAL DEVELOPMENT
APPLIED RESEARCH
FUNDAMENTAL RESEARCH

| SHORT TERM | MEDIUM TERM | LONG TERM |

This is an idealized scenario. Often there is no clear-cut separation between the research types and they don't have to be performed in this sequence. For example, an applied research project might raise a question that is addressed in a fundamental research project.

Who determines what the topic is?

- In **top-down** research calls, the research directions are defined by the sponsoring agency. Even if your project will end world hunger, it will not be funded unless it falls within the scope established by the funding source. These types of calls are typical in applied research and for addressing societal challenges. The involvement of non-academic partners is sometimes a requirement.
- **Bottom-up** calls are researcher-driven and most often used in fundamental research. In such calls, you can propose your own topics and goals as long as they promise to provide a substantial contribution towards the generation of new knowledge in the field. Sometimes the funding agency is willing to sponsor high-risk, high-reward, research proposals.

Research Project Canvas

Project title: **VISION-1**

Problem

What real-world problem are w...
Why should the problem be so...
What is the specific knowledge...

- SELF-DRIVING CARS THREATEN CYCLISTS
- CAN'T READ FACIAL EXPRESSIONS
- CAN'T INTERPRET BODY LANGUAGE

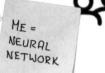

Objectives

What main objective will move us toward solving...
What are the specific sub-objectives of the proje...

Results and Impact

What new knowledge will be generated?
How will the project impact your field and b...
Who benefits and in what way (researchers, ... soc...

Typical results
New methods
New/improved procedures
Code
Models
New knowledge

Possible impacts
Competitive advantage
Environmental or social benefits
Increased awareness
Change in values, beliefs, attitude...
Better education
Economic gains
Policy change

- CYCLIST BODY LANGUAGE RECOGNITION
- OPEN-SOURCE NN CODE FOR SELF-DRIVING CARS
- IMPACT: 70% FEWER CYCLIST INJURIES

Participants

Which key participants will allow us to reach the obj...
What are the strengths of each participant?
What is each partner going to do?
How will partners complement each other?

Key accomplishments
Related publications
Previous teamwork
Consortium strengths
Role of each participant
Noteworthy related resu...

- ME = NEURAL NETWORK
- JANE = BODY-LANGUAGE

Dissemination

Who is the target audience?
How do we reach them?
Who and how will exploit the results?
What knowledge can be shared?
What IP has to be protected?

Typical dissemination means
Scientific journals
Conference presentations
Data repositories
The Internet
Workshops/meetings/web...
Apps/prototypes
Patents
Training
Traditional media

- TRAINING FOR INDUSTRY
- FOUR TOP-LEVEL PAPERS
- PRESS RELEASES FOR GENERAL PUBLIC

Timeline

How long will the project take?
When are specific activities planned to occur?
When will we reach important milestones?
Who contributes what and when?
When does travel take place?

Typical items of a Gantt Chart
Work packages
Tasks
Milestones
Deliverables
Interdependency
Travel

	Y1	Y2	Y3
BODY LANGUAGE	D1		
GESTURES		D2	
RESPONSE			D3

Funder's requirements

What requirements are set by the funding body?
Expected budget? Which costs can be funded?
Key criteria for project evaluation?

Typical requirements Research aims Budget Eligible costs Seniority of ... enti... ... TRL

- INDUSTRY PARTNER
- <500K $

Budget

What are the major expe...
How much will the need...
What is the budget of ea...

- 110K = SCIENTISTS

Example costs Wages Equipment Infrastruc...

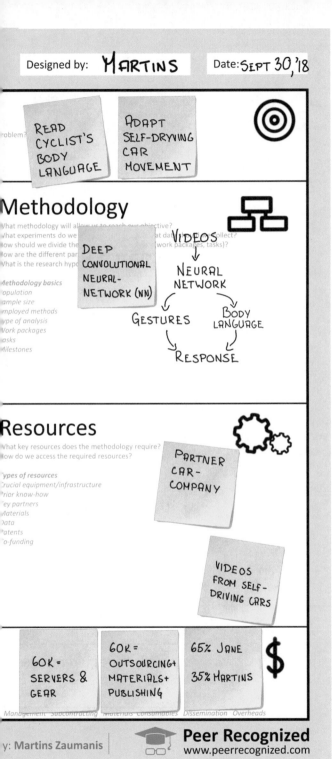

Example Project Canvas

How self-driving cars predict bicycle movements

When human drivers see cyclists, we can easily interpret the cyclist's hand gestures and body language. Self-driving cars struggle with this.

Let's say I want to propose a project to improve the safety of cyclists when encountered by self-driving cars.

The project, which I have given the acronym VISION, is described in this Project Canvas. I have tried to outline every key aspect of the proposal using sticky notes, hand-drawn images of the core methodology and created a rough timeline for a three-year project.

As I methodically progressed through the blocks, **I made sure that they were interconnected**. For example, I aligned the methodology with the objectives, included the items from the methodology in the timeline, and made sure that the results and impact solved the problems I identified.

53

Connect the Project Canvas Blocks

First think about and then fill in each of the Project Canvas blocks. Once all of the blocks have the required information, ensure they are well interconnected. The Project Canvas blocks are organized so that the most related aspects of a project are laid out across **four main axes**.

Don't be afraid to place similar sticky notes in several blocks. In fact, this indicates that you have come up with a well-rounded proposal.

The **Results and their Impact** must help solve the identified **Problem** and the **Dissemination** strategy should be set up to broadcast the results to audiences most affected by the problem.

The **Funder's requirements** can set boundaries for any of the blocks.

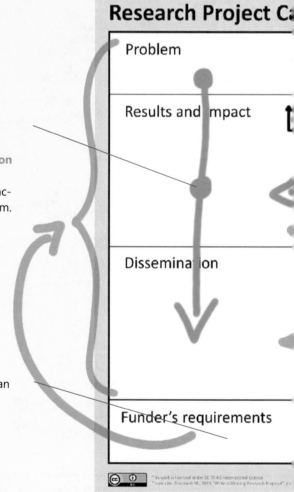

Research Project Ca

Problem

Results and impact

Dissemination

Funder's requirements

The **Objectives** should be closely linked to the identified **Problem**.

The **Methodology** should allow reaching the set **Objectives**, and the required **Resources** should be available to execute the methodology.

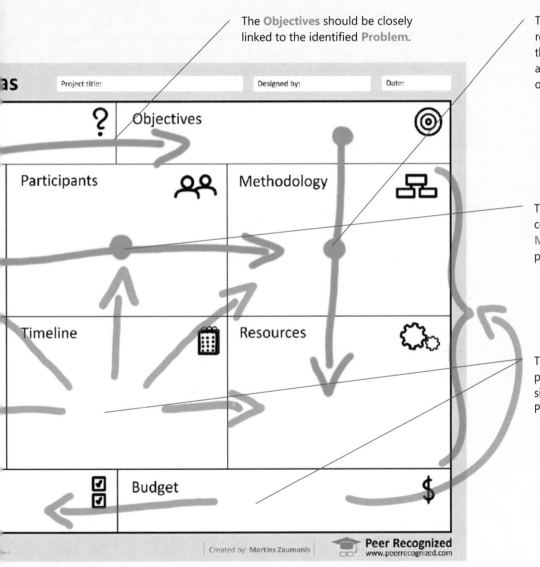

as

Project title: Designed by: Date:

? Objectives ◎

Participants 👥   Methodology 🖧

Timeline 📅   Resources ⚙

☑☑ Budget $

Created by: Martins Zaumanis

Peer Recognized
www.peerrecognized.com

The **Participants** should have the competence to execute the **Methodology** and deliver the planned **Results**.

The **Budget** and **Timeline** aspects of a project must be considered at almost all the other Project Canvas blocks.

Filling the Project Canvas

The primary objective for filling out Project Canvas is to serve as the outline for writing a successful proposal. But this is not all that the Canvas can do for you.

In the following pages, I will show you three ways you can benefit from using the Project Canvas. Later on, in Part III you will see how to use the Project Canvas for generating and rating your research ideas.

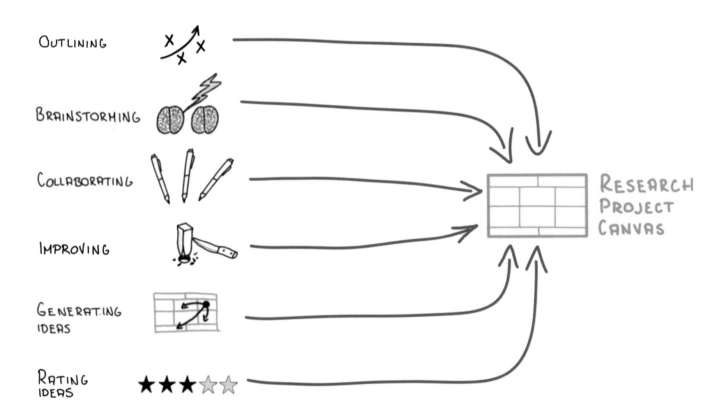

STICKY NOTES + RESEARCH PROJECT CANVAS = LOVE ♡

PRINT A LARGE PROJECT CANVAS AND ATTACH IT TO A WALL OR RECREATE THE PROJECT CANVAS ON A WHITEBOARD

USE A SINGLE STICKY NOTE FOR EACH IDEA - THIS WAY YOU CAN MOVE THINGS AROUND EASILY

USE DIFFERENT COLOR STICKY NOTES FOR DIFFERENT ASPECTS OF THE PROPOSAL (RESEARCH OBJECTIVE, WORK PACKAGES, INSTITUTIONS, ETC.). THIS WILL ENSURE THAT EACH TOPIC IS FULLY EXPLORED WITHIN THE PROJECT CANVAS

DRAW WHEN POSSIBLE

BE SPECIFIC AND CONCISE - NO LONG SENTENCES

Use the Project Canvas for Brainstorming

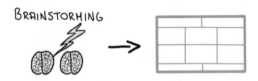

The exercise of filling in the Research Project Canvas will force you to define the problem clearly, specify who cares about it, and explore how it could be solved. You will also be forced to think about practical aspects, like having the required expertise, tools, time, and funding to execute the research. This process will help you generate new ideas and refine the existing ones.

Importantly, the Project Canvas will reveal if something isn't going to work so that you don't waste your time on a proposal destined for failure. For example, it might be that you simply do not have the resources needed to deliver the anticipated results. Or that the project duration set by the funding agency is not enough time to solve the problem. Finding such dead ends right at the start is exactly what you want! It is better to find the challenges before you have invested days or weeks writing a full proposal. Since the Project Canvas only requires one page, you can come up with multiple variations in a couple of hours to help you decide which approach you like the best.

*When **generating ideas**, don't think too much about the details. Focus on the blocks that are most important for your project. At this stage, quantity is important so feel free to embrace wild ideas.*

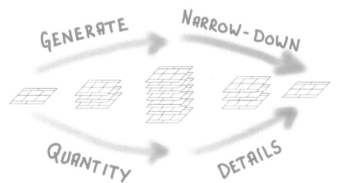

*Once you have generated a pile of research ideas, take a fresh look and **narrow them down** to the most promising options that you can refine later. In Part III of this book, I will introduce the Proposal Review Checklist that can help with this process.*

Two Parts of the Project Canvas

SHOULD WE DO THIS?   CAN WE DO THIS?

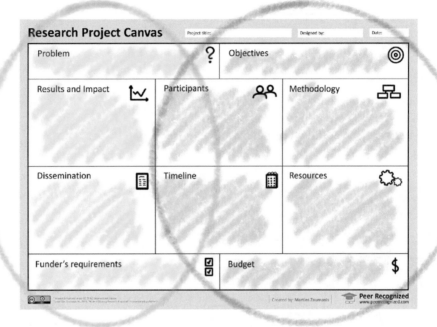

The left side of the Research Project Canvas covers the Reasons we *Should do this:*

- The project is tackling an important problem.
- The project can reasonably be expected to deliver the anticipated results.
- The results are going to impact the community, the sponsor, or science in general, and their dissemination will have an impact.
- The proposed research fulfills the funder's requirements.

The right side of the Research Project Canvas deals with the aspect of *Can we do this:*

- The proposed methodology and available resources can achieve the defined objectives.
- You or your team are the right people to tackle the problem.
- The research can be performed in a timely and cost-efficient manner.

Use the Project Canvas to Collaborate

It is rare that a scientist writes a research project proposal single-handedly. Often you will have a supervisor, colleagues, or external partners who contribute, or at least help with improving it prior to submission.

Jointly fill the Project Canvas

Before you start writing the proposal, sit down with everyone involved and fill the Project Canvas blocks together. If you already have a good idea about the structure of the proposal, you might want to bring a draft version that everyone can discuss and improve upon.

 For online meetings, use the **digital whiteboard version of the Research Project Canvas**. It allows everyone to contribute to the Project Canvas simultaneously. You can access it here: https://peerrecognized.com/projectcanvas

Filling in the Project Canvas will be especially helpful for interdisciplinary projects. In such teams, where everyone's an expert in something else, merging the ideas into a coherent proposal can be tough. The Project Canvas will help direct the separate parts of the proposal towards a common goal.

The rigid requirements of the Project Canvas will make the effort to come up with solutions more productive. As opposed to the usual rambling, everyone can see that there are empty spaces that have to be filled and no one gets to go home before the blocks make sense. This promotes finding compromises and getting the job done.

Jointly write the proposal

The jointly-filled Project Canvas will help serve as a guide for a proposal structure that everyone agrees on. By looking at the Project Canvas, you will remember what to write in the proposal and the contents of the written document will not come as a surprise to anyone. This way, you can minimize the chances of disagreements among the participants later on in the writing process.

If multiple people are involved in writing the proposal you can use the pre-filled Project Canvas to distribute the proposal writing workload and set deadlines. Simply decide who is converting a certain part of the Project Canvas into a written text and when it is due.

 Making use of collaborative writing tools prevents the hassle of merging multiple documents. You will find a list of the most useful **collaborative writing tools** here: http://peerrecognized.com/projectcanvas

Show previous teamwork

Achieving the planned research results is not merely a sum of the technical skills of individual project participants. It is only when the researchers enjoy working together that you can expect noteworthy findings. Reviewers are aware of this beneficial symbiosis, so make sure to mention any previous collaboration (projects, papers, visits) amongst those involved in the proposal.

Use the Canvas to Improve a Proposal

Everyone has a plan until they get punched in the face.

Mike Tyson meant this literally, but in the context of a research proposal, this will (hopefully) be just a metaphor. Still, running into a dead-end halfway through a carefully crafted research project or receiving a negative review can be just as demoralizing as a punch in the face. While boxers can revert to their instincts after receiving a punch, I suggest you fall back to the Research Project Canvas rather than go down for the count.

Use the Project Canvas to refocus

First, identify the troublesome block(s) in the Project Canvas that are the key problems of your proposal. Next, use the Project Canvas to re-think the approach you should take, or refocus your efforts on other parts of the proposal to see if you can circumvent the problem.

The Project Canvas will also help you to prioritize your efforts for a running project. For example:

• Need to finish the project before your contract ends? - Start with the Timeline block.
• Need to find a consensus between the research interests of different partners in a complex project? - Look at the objectives and the methodology blocks and then work your way back.

Improving the Project Canvas

Remember the Project Canvas for the self-driving research project? Let's say I submitted a proposal based on that Project Canvas but it was rejected because the reviewers felt it was not innovative enough.

I, however, still believe in the idea and want to improve and re-submit the proposal. So, I dig up the original Project Canvas and decide to add a new component to the research - that self-driving cars should not only understand cyclist's body language but also communicate with them using pictograms that are displayed on the car's windscreen.

See the improved Project Canvas on the right. Here I use blue color sticky notes for the new research objective. By methodically going through the blocks, I notice that an important resource is missing - I need a sample pool of cyclists who are willing to participate in a questionnaire. But I would also need permission to use their personal data to make sure I comply with data protection rules. Without a plan to deal with this, the reviewers would have a good reason to reject the proposal once again.

Version two of the VISION project on self-driving car interaction with cyclists

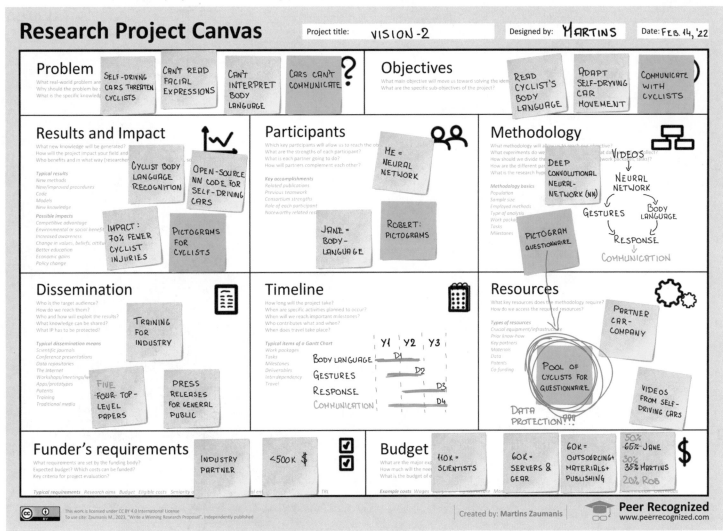

Research Project Canvas

Project title: **VISION-2**

Designed by: **MARTINS**

Date: **FEB. 14, '22**

Problem
What real-world problem are...
Why should the problem be...
What is the specific knowledge...

- SELF-DRIVING CARS THREATEN CYCLISTS
- CAN'T READ FACIAL EXPRESSIONS
- CAN'T INTERPRET BODY LANGUAGE
- CARS CAN'T COMMUNICATE ?

Objectives
What main objective will move us toward solving the ident...
What are the specific sub-objectives of the project?

- READ CYCLIST'S BODY LANGUAGE
- ADAPT SELF-DRIVING CAR MOVEMENT
- COMMUNICATE WITH CYCLISTS

Results and Impact
What new knowledge will be generated?
How will the project impact your field and...
Who benefits and in what way (researcher...

Typical results
New methods
New/improved procedures
Code
Models
New knowledge
Possible impacts
Competitive advantage
Environmental or social benefit
Increased awareness
Change in values, beliefs, attitu...
Better education
Economic gains
Policy change

- CYCLIST BODY LANGUAGE RECOGNITION
- OPEN-SOURCE NN CODE FOR SELF-DRIVING CARS
- IMPACT: 70% FEWER CYCLIST INJURIES
- PICTOGRAMS FOR CYCLISTS

Participants
Which key participants will allow us to reach the ob...
What are the strengths of each participant?
What is each partner going to do?
How will partners complement each other?

Key accomplishments
Related publications
Previous teamwork
Consortium strengths
Role of each participant
Noteworthy related res...

- ME = NEURAL NETWORK
- JANE = BODY-LANGUAGE
- ROBERT: PICTOGRAMS

Methodology
What methodology will allow us to reach our objective?
What experiments do we... that da...
How should we divide the... work packages, tasks)?
How are the different pa...
What is the research hyp...

Methodology basics
Population
Sample size
Employed methods
Type of analysis
Work packages
Tasks
Milestones

- DEEP CONVOLUTIONAL NEURAL-NETWORK (NN)
- PICTOGRAM QUESTIONNAIRE
- VIDEOS → NEURAL NETWORK → GESTURES / BODY LANGUAGE → RESPONSE → COMMUNICATION

Dissemination
Who is the target audience?
How do we reach them?
Who and how will exploit the results?
What knowledge can be shared?
What IP has to be protected?

Typical dissemination means
Scientific journals
Conference presentations
Data repositories
The Internet
Workshops/meetings/we...
Apps/prototypes
Patents
Training
Traditional media

- TRAINING FOR INDUSTRY
- FIVE FOUR TOP-LEVEL PAPERS
- PRESS RELEASES FOR GENERAL PUBLIC

Timeline
How long will the project take?
When are specific activities planned to occur?
When will we reach important milestones?
Who contributes what and when?
When does travel take place?

Typical items of a Gantt Chart
Work packages
Tasks
Milestones
Deliverables
Inter-dependency
Travel

	Y1	Y2	Y3
BODY LANGUAGE	D1		
GESTURES		D2	
RESPONSE			D3
COMMUNICATION			D4

Resources
What key resources does the methodology require?
How do we access the required resources?

Types of resources
Crucial equipment/infrastructure
Prior know-how
Key partners
Materials
Data
Patents
Co-funding

- PARTNER CAR-COMPANY
- POOL OF CYCLISTS FOR QUESTIONNAIRE
- DATA PROTECTION?!!
- VIDEOS FROM SELF-DRIVING CARS

Funder's requirements
What requirements are set by the funding body?
Expected budget? Which costs can be funded?
Key criteria for project evaluation?

Typical requirements Research aims Budget Eligible costs Seniority... ...al ent... ...TRL

- INDUSTRY PARTNER
- <500K $ ☑ ☑

Budget
What are the major exp...
How much will the nee...
What is the budget of e...

Example costs Wages ... ...Infrastructure Man...

- 110K = SCIENTISTS
- 60K = SERVERS & GEAR
- 60K = OUTSOURCING+ MATERIALS+ PUBLISHING
- 50% 65% JANE / 30% 35% MARTINS / 20% ROB

$

Created by: **Martins Zaumanis**

Peer Recognized
www.peerrecognized.com

I will post **examples of Research Project Canvases** for different proposals on the book website. I would love to also include your Project Canvas there so please use the hashtag #PeerRecognized when you post on social media or you can upload a picture of your work on: https://peerrecognized.com/projectcanvas

I would enjoy to see how you use Project Canvas. Send me a photo: martins@peerrecognized.com

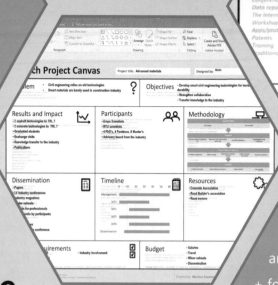

Different ways of working on the Project Canvas

Draw the Project Canvas on a whiteboard and use markers to fill it

+ for group sessions if you don't have a plotter available

- need to take a picture and can not easily edit it afterwards

Click the three dots to download the Canvas

Print the Project Canvas and fill in the blocks with a pen or pencil

+ ideal for quick brainstorming

- the pieces of paper can get disorganized

Print the Project Canvas on a large piece of paper and attach it to the wall. Use sticky notes or a pen for writing

+ ideal for in-person team sessions

- not everyone has a plotter

Project the Canvas on a screen or on a projector.
Use sticky notes

+ ideal for conference rooms

- make sure the sticky notes stick to the screen but don't leave marks afterwards

Use PowerPoint and fill it in using text boxes

+ ensures you can easily save a digital version of the Project Canvas

- somewhat slower than writing on a paper for quick brainstorming

Use an online whiteboard for group editing

+ ideal for online meetings

- in-person meetings encourage more interaction

#PeerRecognized

WRITE YOUR PROPOSAL

The first time I found myself reviewing proposals for the leading European research funding scheme, Horizon (the equivalent to NSF grant in the US), my task was to rate nine proposals.

I read the first one and it was great: the methodology was well thought out, the research team was excellent and, should the planned results be achieved, the impact would be enormous. I gave the proposal the maximum score.

Then I read the second proposal. I was just as great. The third - same again. I started to see a pattern.

In the end, out of the nine proposals, only one was clearly below par. Any of the eight others could have been supported and yet, as is always the case, there was not enough funding for all of them. My difficult job was to decide between eight proposals, any of which were worthy of support.

***

So far we have discussed the process of using the Research Project Canvas to conceptualize research ideas. We have also established what is expected from each section of a proposal and mapped the Project Canvas blocks into the typical structure of a grant application.

I could have ended the book here with the certainty that proposals based on the described principles would be very good. The problem is, there are a lot of very good proposals out there and to maximize your chances of being selected for funding, yours has to be more than *very good*.

Your proposal has to stand out from other proposals that are equally worthy. Otherwise, you are at a risk of being one of the applicants that is given the most frustrating feedback of them all:

> *Your proposal received a high score but due to the unavailable funding, it can not be supported.*

That's why I also need to show you writing principles for making your application stand out. For implementing most of the principles, we will rely on a filled Research Project Canvas.

Proposal writing template

On the webpage http://peerrecognized.com/ projectcanvas you can download **a template for writing research proposals**. It is tailored to the Project Canvas and holds writing tips from this book. It also helps with helps with formatting. Use this template only if the funder does not provide their own.

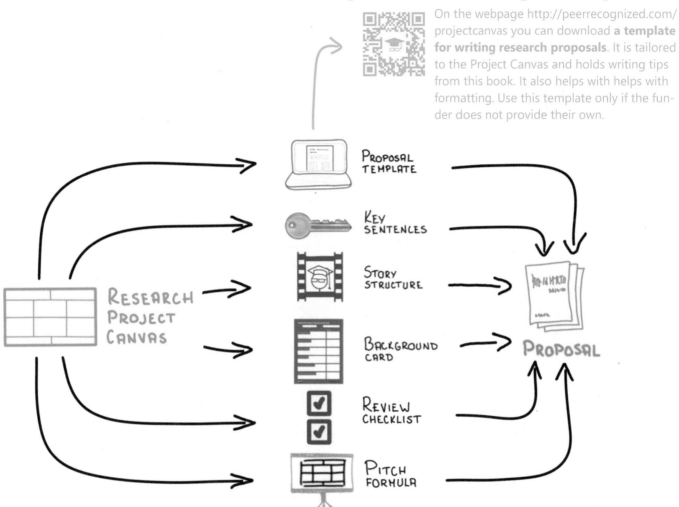

How much time does writing a proposal take?

How much time you need to write a proposal depends on the complexity of the research, the supplementary documents required, the partnerships involved, and obviously your writing speed. It can vary dramatically. I have been able to write a small career grant in just one day, while a multi-partner proposal has taken half a year to put together.

Compose the Key Sentences

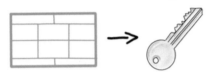

Your Research Project Canvas blocks should be filled with short phrases or drawings. Once you have them, you can kick off the writing process by converting each Canvas block into proposal text using a *Key Sentence**.

Written well, these sentences will hold all the key information about your proposal. You will know that the sentences are complete if you are able to bind them together and use them as a short summary of your research.

The Key Sentences are a great way to help kick off the writing process since you will no longer be staring at a blank screen. After finalizing the sentences, your next

task will be to add more detail so as to demonstrate to reviewers that the sentences are true.

You just need to paste the sentences into the respective section of the proposal and start expanding upon them.

For each Project Canvas block, I will provide you with a Key Sentence skeleton that you can use to then adapt the sentence for your own proposal. To make the key sentence idea more tangible, I also provide a sample sentence for each Project Canvas block from the self-driving project VISION example.

 You can access the **Key Sentence templates** in the proposal writing template at http://peerrecognized.com/projectcanvas

Problem

Key sentence example

Self-driving cars have difficulties predicting the movement of cyclists thus endangering this vulnerable traffic user group; the main problem lies in the fact that self-driving cars are not able to read the body language of cyclists to predict their intentions.

Structure

The [huge real-world problem that clearly needs to be solved]; [a specific knowledge-gap within the huge problem that you plan to address in your project].

* I adapted the Key Sentences from Parker Derrington Ltd, https://parkerderrington.com/key-sentence-skeletons/

Objective

Key sentence example

With the VISION project, we aim to improve the prediction of cyclist's movements by self-driving cars. To achieve this aim, we have two specific objectives:

1. *Develop an algorithm that recognizes hand gestures, head movements, and velocity changes of cyclists and interprets them to anticipate their driving intentions.*

2. *Develop an algorithm that adapts the self-driving car movement based on the predicted bicycle movement.*

Structure

With the [title/acronym] **project we aim to** [what the project is going to develop/achieve/discover/establish/improve/analyze to solve some part of the identified research gap]. **To achieve this aim, we have** [number] **specific objectives**:

1. [Develop/achieve/discover/establish/improve/analyze] [the objective of the first sub-project]

2. [Develop/achieve/discover/establish/improve/analyze] [the objective of the second sub-project]

3. ...

Methodology

Key sentence example

During the VISION project, we will use real-world videos provided by a project partner to train a deep convolutional neural network in classifying body language and hand gestures of cyclists.

We will then build a response model to adjust the car's movement based on the predictions.

Structure

During the project [description of research activity] **to** [state what will the activity achieve].

[Repeat this structure for each key methodology element that is employed to reach the objectives].

Resources

Key sentence example

The project will use videos from a project partner - self-driving car company - to first develop and then test the developed algorithms.

Structure

The project will [use/ apply/ benefit from] **to** [specific outcome]

Participants

Key sentence example

The principal investigator of the project, Dr. Jane Goodrich from Peer Recognized Academy, is an expert in social behavior who has been awarded the AAAI distinguished service award and has published 19 papers on the subject of mathematically classifying facial expressions.

Structure

[Role], [Person's name] **from** [affiliation, if there is more than one partner] **is** [core area of expertise] **and has** [proof of expertise in terms of publications, projects, awards, etc.].

[Repeat this for each key person.]

Results and Impact

Key sentence example

The project will result in a computer code that allows real-time prediction of cyclist's movement, including:

1.   A convolutional neural network model that classifies cyclist's body language and hand gestures to predict their movement.

2.   A response model that can be implemented into self-driving car software to adapt car trajectory and velocity based on the predicted cyclist's movements.

Delivering the code and publishing it in an open-access repository will enable any self-driving car company to implement it into the car's decision-making process for improving the safety of cyclists.

Structure

The project will [a general statement of what results/deliverables/outcomes the project will deliver to solve the problem you identified]**, including:**

1.   [a statement of delivering a specific result/outcome in response to the objective No.1]

2.   [a statement of delivering a specific result/outcome in response to the objective No.2]

3.   ...

Delivering these results/outcomes will [enable/allow/...] [specify the stakeholder] **to** [explain what positive impacts these results promise].

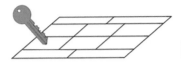

Dissemination

Key sentence example

We will disseminate the project results through leading scientific journals and academic conferences in the machine learning field; demonstrate the capabilities of the developed algorithm in a closed test site; and communicate the project's activities to society through press releases.

Structure

We will [the relevant activity] **the project results within** [the key target audience] **through** [the channels that you plan to use].

Timeline

Key sentence example

The project will start in June 2024, it will be executed within 36 months with periodic reports submitted to the funding agency after reaching milestone one in month 12, and milestone two in month 21.

Structure

The project will start in [date], **it will be executed in** [number of months], **and** [add the time when key reports/milestones/deliverables/other critical accomplishments will be submitted/reached].

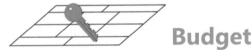

Budget

Key sentence example

The total eligible project costs are 250,531 USD where 107,480 USD are devoted to personnel costs, 59,000 USD to purchasing new equipment, 25,000 USD are material costs, 6,000 USD are for subcontracting costs, 28,000 USD are dissemination costs, and 25,051 are indirect costs. The Peer Recognized Academy will use 66 % of the budget and the Research University will use 34%. 10% of the costs are covered through an in-kind contribution from the Self-Driving Car Association.

Structure

The total eligible project costs are [the sum] **where** [name the cost for each cost category as requested in the research call guide]. [Name of Partner 1] **will use** [X]**% of the budget,** [Name of Partner #2] **will use** [X]**% of the budget.** [describe co-financing by the partners, if any]. [X]**% of the costs are covered through** [the funder, if already known]

Visualize Important Concepts

Flowcharts, diagrams, schematics, tables, and illustrations are extremely useful for quickly conveying information about your proposal and can serve as a natural focus point.

A good image can also save a lot of space when compared to expressing the same information in text. This is especially important in proposals because funding agencies almost always enforce a strict page (or character) limit.

Since people typically remember visuals more vividly than we remember text, including clear images might just be the little push that helps the reviewers lean towards preferring your proposal.

Good images also come in handy when you need to present the proposal to someone in-person. For example, to partners you want to invite to participate, to your supervisor, or to a grant review committee.

Learning about illustration in science

The second book in the *Peer Recognized* series offers a blueprint for converting scientific concepts into self-explanatory diagrams. The book *Research Data Visualization and Scientific Graphics* will also help you turn dry research data into convincing data charts. Get it here: https://peerrecognized.com/book2

I highly recommend that you read the book but, since scientific graphic design is central to the success of a research proposal, I shall give you a brief overview. The cheat-sheet to the right offers a summary of effective visualization principles and summarizes the eleven main types of graphics that you could use for a proposal.

Scientific graphic design

Read the book "Research Data Visualization and Scientific Graphics" by Martins Zaumanis to learn more

VISUALIZATION PRINCIPLES

START WITH A SKETCH

A sketch

✓Use pen and paper to draw the first sketch. This allows to experiment with the concept and layout

✓A sketch can also help to develop new research ideas and refine existing ones

Layout

✓The layout should guide the eyes of the viewer on a journey across the graphic

✓Achieve this using the different visualization principles mentioned here

DRAW ATTENTION

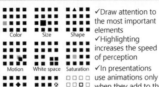

Color   Size   Shape

Motion   White space   Saturation

Orientation   Added mark   Line width

✓Draw attention to the most important elements

✓Highlighting increases the speed of perception

✓In presentations use animations only when they add to the message

GRAPHICAL FEATURES

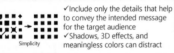

Simplicity

✓Include only the details that help to convey the intended message for the target audience

✓Shadows, 3D effects, and meaningless colors can distract

Visual order

✓Align items, keep lines parallel and straight, and use the same perspective for all the elements

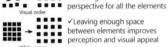

White space

✓Leaving enough space between elements improves perception and visual appeal

Discrete steps

✓Schematics, flow charts, and diagrams can benefit from the introduction of discrete steps (numbering, arrows, framing, grouping, and enclosure)

Hierarchy

✓Use larger shapes, thicker lines, bold/larger font to create hierarchy

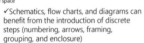

Annotations

✓Annotations help the to make sense of visual information

When writing on a busy background (e.g. a microscopy image), add text outline or white glow to ensure enough contrast

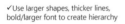

Flow

✓Use arrows to show a sequence of events, connect elements, demonstrate a change, or draw attention to important features

GROUP

Group elements to show connections, introduce discrete steps, and create structure

Proximity   Shading   Similarity   Enclosure   Connection

Color

MATRIX

✓Summarize research results

✓Provide ranking

✓Compare categories

✓Use arrows, crosses, checkmarks, rating bars, and color coding to convey the information

SCHEMATIC

✓Only include relevant elements

✓Distort the elements, if necessary

GRAPHIC TYPES

FLOW CHART

✓Summarize models, methods or concepts

✓Show interconnections

✓Map decision process

✓Show workflow

✓Best used in the methodology section papers and in research proposals.

METAPHORICAL DIAGRAM

Leverage familiar shapes to:

✓Simplify complex ideas

✓Show conceptual relationships

✓Create associations

✓Best used in proposals and presentations

VISUALIZATION

✓Create a "reality feeling" of a research result

✓Can use when a photography is impossible

✓Demonstrate application of a research result

DRAWING

✓Illustrate research concepts

✓Demonstrate research approach

✓Simple to create using basic software

DISGUISED DIAGRAM

✓Show hierarchy

✓Indicate importance

✓Demonstrate relationships

✓Familiar shapes ease perception

MAP

✓Demonstrate results

✓Show location

✓Put research in a geographical context

✓Show a geographical trend or connections

IMAGE

✓Explain a particular phenomena

✓Demonstrate test setup

✓Show an important case or procedure

✓Add annotations to in figure or caption

✓Include scale and labels, when appropriate

SUPERIMPOSED IMAGE

✓Layer elements on an image

✓Zoom to show details

✓Highlight particular parts

✓Explain the manipulations to avoid misleading

GENERIC PHOTO

✓Provide context, show the impact

✓Best used in presentations and in online communication

Peer Recognized

www.peerrecognized.com

You can download the **Scientific Graphic Design cheat sheet** through
http://peerrecognized.com/projectcanvas

The power of a flowchart

A proposal could potentially use any of the eleven graphic types included in the cheat sheet, but one stands out. A flow chart is an extremely effective and efficient way to provide an overview of a research proposal and to summarize the planned methodology. Assess whether or not you can demonstrate some of the following items using a flowchart:

- What are the main activities of the research?
- How are different parts of the project intertwined and geared to reaching the defined goal?
- Which interconnections between various activities are the most important?
- What core concepts are the activities focused around?
- Who are the partners? Can their contribution be linked directly to individual tasks within the project?
- What are the expected results of the project and what impact will they have?

On the opposite page are example flowcharts from research proposals. Feel free to use them as an inspiration, but also look around on the internet and you should find many more examples.

Flowcharts facilitate discussion

While I was writing this chapter I was also helping to write a research proposal involving two institutions and five researchers.

For the first couple of meetings we were rambling on about the proposal and somehow already had a first written draft. But the methodology was always raising questions. It was not clear what tests we should use and why, what materials to test, and who will do what.

So I drafted a methodology flowchart and, after showing this to the partners, the discussion became much clearer.

Sketch it first

Personally, I like to create a draft overview figure before writing even a line of text for a proposal. Such a visual definition of the core concept of my proposal helps add structure to my writing and ensures that the proposal is easy to follow.

Don't try to create a polished overview chart right from the onset. For the writing process, it is better to start with a sketch. Unlike a finalized figure, a sketch can be easily adapted as your ideas evolve during the writing and thought formation process.

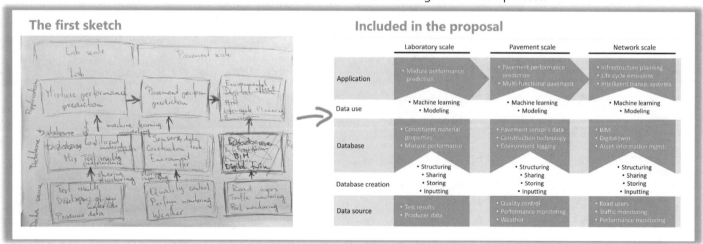

The first sketch **Included in the proposal**

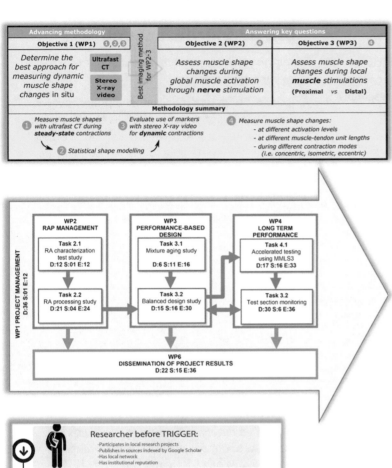

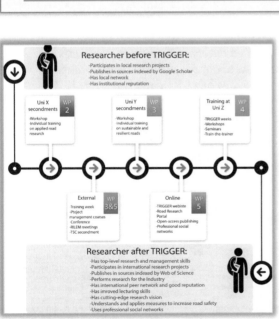

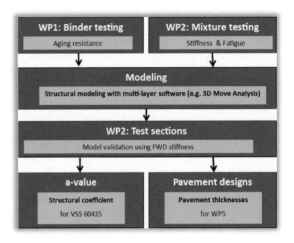

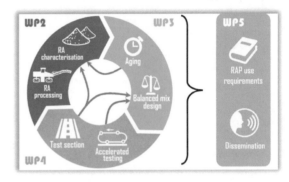

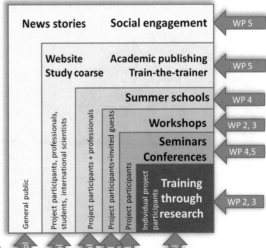

Top left flowchart: Aeles, Van Wassenbergh, Aerts: MSCA Individual Fellowships - MSCA–PF21, I-MUSCLE; funded by European Commission

Other charts: Martins Zaumanis

Less is more...

Research projects can be quite complicated. The principal investigator has to decide on the research boundary conditions, consider which variables to include, interpret research findings, deal with constrained resources, mediate the expectations of project participants, comply with safety requirements, and juggle many other decisions. If one would try to put it in a flowchart, you might end up with one resembling the figure below.

...but be specific enough

Simplifying a chart, however, should not mean that it loses important content.

A good test to determine whether a project overview illustration includes enough details is to first imagine that another researcher is writing a proposal on the same topic. If they are able to use the same image for their proposal without much change, it is not detailed enough.

While this multifaceted flowchart might accurately describe how research projects end up being executed, such a level of complexity is most likely going to just confuse reviewers.

Too general

This is a chart I once included in a draft proposal. A partner rightfully pointed out that such a figure was not detailed enough for our project.

Enough details

So I modified the chart. The new chart includes more details about our project. This gave reviewers a far better idea of what we were about.

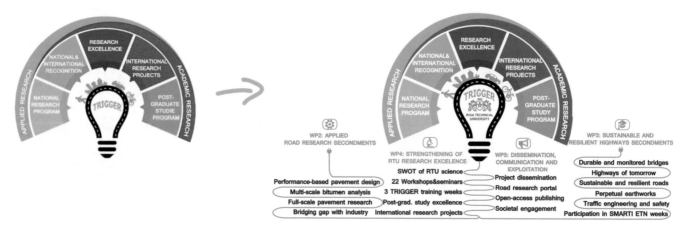

A Table

A table is another graphic element that helps add structure to your proposal. For example, you could create:

- A table listing the objectives, tasks, and the corresponding methodologies.
- A table including the expected results and their impact.
- A table summarizing the deliverables and milestones, their planned delivery date, and the responsible person for each.
- A table displaying the professional profiles of the main scientists and the tasks they are involved in.
- A table with the proposed dissemination activities and the target groups they will reach.
- A table summarizing the staff efforts for each work package.
- A budget table which includes justification of each cost item.
- A table showing the project's execution risks (both technical and administrative), their impact, and mitigation measures.
- A table summarizing how a topic defined in a top-down research call is addressed.
- A table summarizing training activities.
- A schedule table which shows time, location, and participants for planned meetings.

Work Package	Research need	Proposed solution in the project
RA processing	RA stockpiles are not homogeneous and high RA fines content limit maximum RA content in asphalt mixtures	Determine optimum milling conditions using experimental jobsite. Compare different innovative RA processing technologies available at partner's jobsites.
RA characterization	RA characterization is time consuming and not frequent enough	Apply simplified tests for determining homogeneity: fragmentation test and cohesion test [30].
Aging	Aging significantly affects the performance-based test results.	Adopt an aging procedure before testing performance-based properties. This will be based on RILEM STAR report No.9 [31], and CEN 12697-52.
Balanced mix design	Designing of high RA mixtures using volumetric design methods can lead to premature pavement failure	Use balanced mix design method with performance tests: semi-circular bend test for cracking, French wheel tester for rutting, TSRST for low temperature cracking. Develop a mix design and approval procedure.
Accelerated testing	Lack of trust in long-term performance of high RA mixtures.	Use Model Mobile Load Simulator (MMLS3) to determine the life cycle of high RA mixtures compared to conventional mixes. The mix design procedures will be validated as a result.
Test section	A full-scale demonstrator is necessary to validate the developed RA characterization and mix design procedures.	Test mix composition materials and produced mixture using the developed procedures. Monitor pavement performance.

Here is an example table defining the research needs and solutions that I proposed for one of my projects.

Tell a Story

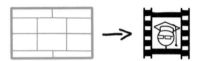

Grant writing has to, by definition, be done in a different style than the writing of research papers. Papers describe something that was done in the past while grant proposals are proposing something that will take place in the future. Warping the space-time to put reviewers in the future where you have been awarded the grant and accomplished whatever you wished for would be ideal. But since that's not possible yet, admitting that a grant application is basically a story is your second best option.

The word *story* still has a negative connotation among scientists. To many it feels like fiction; something that is not real; something that is invented, or perhaps exaggerated.

Researchers feel that they are not here to tell stories. We have to be factual and impartial. Right? Right.

But so do journalists and authors of nonfiction. The very concept of non-fiction revolves around stories which are objective and true, just like the proposals that scientists should write.

Thinking of a proposal as a story is one technique which can give you that little bit of an edge to move your proposal from the category of *good* to the category of *funded*.

Why is that? Well, scientists are trained to think that evidence and logic are all that is needed to convince others. To my own dismay, this is not the case.

Humans, including scientists (yes, even you and me), rarely make decisions based purely on logic. There is even evidence that our brain is physically incapable of making any decision based on facts alone*. People inevitably are influenced by emotions when making decisions.

My point is that, besides facts and logic, which are by all means the standard approach for convincing reviewers, it will help you to think of your proposal in terms of a story, so as to evoke emotions.

Of course, you don't have to learn how to sensitively describe light shining off a broken piece of glass on a warm summer night (perhaps if you are researching electromagnetic radiation and heat waves you do).

What you can borrow from story-telling is how to maintain an overall structure that is exciting to read, how to place the spotlight on the main items of the proposal (i.e. lead actors), and how to create a great summary (i.e. movie trailer).

Thinking about your proposal in terms of a story is more of an attitude change than anything else. It just helps you realize that a proposal has to be tied together, with each separate part adding more details about the research journey you are planning, each day getting you a bit closer to the desired solution (read: fulfilling the objective).

This slight change in mindset will make your proposal more enjoyable to read for the reviewers. They will better envision how the beginning is tied to the end and how the world will change because of the success that your results promise.

*Gupta et. al. The amygdala and decision-making. 2011, *Neuropsychologia. 49(4):760-6.*

Proposal structure = story structure

Robert McKee, one of the most respected storytelling lecturers in Hollywood explains* that a good story starts with a balance that is disturbed by a surprising event. In response to the surprise, hard decisions have to be made, and great risks need to be taken, all despite working with scarce resources. This journey results in a solution that introduces a new balance and provides new knowledge.

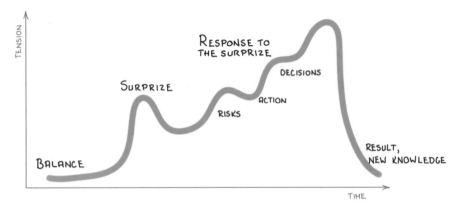

Appreciate just how much the story structure has in common with a research proposal.

A story	A proposal	Canvas part	Story plot example for the self-driving proposal
Balance	The background and problem		Cyclists are not safe in interactions with self-driving cars.
Surprise	The specific research gap		Unlike human drivers, self-driving cars are blind to predicting cyclists' intentions.
Response to the surprise	The way of solving the problem, including objective, methodology, resources, and researchers, all within the constraints of cost, time, and other requirements		Deep convolutional neural network is used to recognize hand gestures and body language of cyclists from videos provided by a project partner. Once done, a code is written for self-driving cars to adapt their movement based on the prediction. All of this is accomplished by two brilliant scientists within three years' time.
Solution	The expected results, their impact, and dissemination		The algorithm for recognizing cyclists' body language is made open-access, and car companies implement it, thus improving traffic safety for all.

*Fryer, Storytelling That Moves People. June 2003, Harvard Business Review

Show the trailer

In his award-winning book *Thinking, Fast and Slow* psychologist and Nobel prize winner Prof. Kahneman remembers that he used to grade the students' exams *the traditional way*. He picked up one test booklet and read all the student's essays one after another. Then he would pick up the next student's booklets and repeat.

When analyzing the scores of his students, he noticed that the results for the essays of a particular student were generally quite consistent. Thinking back about the process, he realized that this happened because when reading the first essay of a particular student he would put this student in a certain mental category. If the first essay was good, encountering a vague statement in the next one did not seem so bad. Clearly, a student who wrote a brilliant first essay deserved the benefit of the doubt for a small failure in the second essay.

If, on the other hand, the student had a bad first essay, a great argument in the next one seemed like a lucky strike.

The halo effect means that the first page of the proposal should be polished to perfection. The reviewers might unconsciously put the proposal into support or no-support category early on when reading the proposal. If your first page is not convincing, they will spend the rest of the review searching for arguments that justify their decision to decline funding.

Of course, this is a wrong approach. If a professor has to rate two essays from a single student - one good and one bad - the grade will change depending on which essay he reads first. This psychological bias is known as the *Halo effect*.

Daniel Kahneman is a Nobel prize-winning professor in psychology. If he was making such a mistake, you can be sure that the proposal reviewers will do so as well. For this reason, it is important to start strong.

*Kahneman, Thinking, Fast and Slow. 2013, *Farrar, Straus and Giroux*

The Drop

Now that I have hopefully convinced you about the importance of the first page, let's see how reimagining the proposal as a story can help you to improve what you write.

The aforementioned structure *balance-surprise-response to the surprise-result* is followed by any story, but not necessarily in this order.

Think of the movie *Fight Club* as an example. It starts with a scene where someone is holding a gun into a sweating man's mouth. This introduction peaks the viewer's interest right before the scene is interrupted and the viewers are sent back in time to chronologically show how the man eventually got into this precarious situation.

Now imagine a scene involving a child riding unsteadily along a city street on a bicycle. A car, identified by a shot of the interior as a self-driving vehicle, approaches the child at the speed of surrounding traffic. Tense music plays. Cutaway shot to lab testing facility.

This story structure is known by the Latin name *In Media Res** but since my Latin is a little dusty, I will call it *The Drop*. The Drop structure is well suited for a research proposal because it introduces the reviewer to the core concept of the proposal right from the beginning. If the drop is interesting enough, you will have the reviewer's attention long enough to step back and provide more context and details in the following pages.

Some agencies require you to submit an abstract or a summary of the proposal. This is where you can use The Drop structure. But even if the first section is something that does not require summarizing the project (e.g. it's a literature review), it is still a good idea to subtly make use of The Drop.

What to include in The Drop?

For a typical research proposal, you first want to provide the reviewers with the context of the research by demonstrating the urgency of the problem you plan to solve. The re-

viewers need to see the overall forest before focusing on specific trees.

In the following sentences, you can quickly reveal the core concept of the research methodology. Finally, you can describe the expected results and demonstrate how solving the problem will advance knowledge in your research field, or how it will benefit society in general. In short, do your best to answer the three basic questions shown in the figure below.

When answering these questions, try to demonstrate the strengths of your proposal. Deciding on the strengths, however, is a more challenging question than it may initially seem.

This is because, out of your entire well-rounded proposal for which you have considered every little detail, you need to restrict yourself to picking just those focus points which have the highest chance of intriguing the reviewers. This means it's time to select your lead actors.

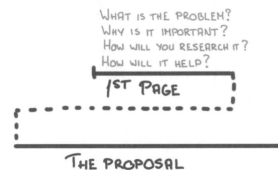

You will find it easier to summarize the project once the bulk of the proposal is almost written and well-organized in your head.

The lead actors

The best movies often have just a few lead actors around whom the film revolves. To effectively apply this concept to *the Drop* and your proposal's story in general, you will have to decide which are the lead actors of your project. This will take you a long way towards turning your proposal into a box office hit (attract funding).

The exercise of defining the lead actors will help you write the first page, the summary, the abstract, and even the title. These parts are typically short but notoriously challenging to write because of their importance.

Which Project Canvas blocks you select to be the lead actors will depend on the type of project you want to carry out. The focus points might even change for the exact same exact proposal depending on which agency you are submitting to.

In the table on the right, you see some example projects and the three leading roles an author could select for each of them. By no means is it meant to show you the correct lead actors. Situations can vary and you need to make your own decision.

The table is only intended to give you some ideas about the broad variety of project types that a researcher might encounter and how the lead actors can change in different situations.

The lead actors in most research projects are not the scientists themselves (unless it's a career advancement grant of some sort). Depending on the project type, the lead actors can be found in any of the Project Canvas blocks.

Project example	Three main Canvas blocks	Lead actors from the Canvas
A traditional research project to address a known research gap in your field		**(Problem)** An important knowledge gap that needs to be filled... **(Methodology)** ...for which you have devised the appropriate methodology... **(Results & Impact)** ...and the results will be very useful for your field.
A mobility grant for doing part of your Ph.D. at some famous professor's lab		**(Resources)** You will have access to some great advice... **(Problem)** ...which will allow you to solve this big problem... **(Participants)** ...and by doing so will allow you to acquire new skills.
A clinical trial for a vaccine during a pandemic		**(Problem)** There is a pandemic... **(Timeline)** ...and you must quickly develop a vaccine... **(Results & Impact)** ...that will reduce infections and deaths.
Application to buy new testing equipment for your lab		**(Resources)** You need to get this uniquely useful machine... **(Result)** ...that will allow you to produce useful results... **(Problem)** ...to solve a specific urgent need.
A research objectives statement for a scholarship application (or tenure track research statement)		**(Participants)** You are highly motivated... **(Objectives)** ...and have clear career goals... **(Problem)** ...that will help to solve this big problem.
A research proposal submitted to a private company for developing a new patentable technology		**(Results)** You will develop a new technology... **(Dissemination)** ...that the company will be able to patent... **(Budget)** ...and earn a lot of money that will justify the expense.
Proposal for an international training network for Ph.D. students		**(Results)** The students will acquire new skills and contacts... **(Methodology)** ...by working on the problems they define themselves... **(Resources)** ...under the supervision of our group of experienced scientists at five different universities.

Describe the Background

The *Problem* block of the Project Canvas is where you will outline the core motivation of the research study by first answering the question *Why should the project be done in the first place?* The answer is certainly a big part of the background section, but there is more to it.

Unless the reviewers are convinced that you are proficient in the research domain, they will never believe that you can offer a meaningful contribution that will advance your scientific field. You could be at risk of repeating whatever someone else has already done, or gathering uninformed observations without being able to fit them into a scientific paradigm. To convince the reviewers otherwise, you must show background knowledge.

Key pieces of a powerful background section:

- Convince the reviewer of the urgency of the problem and the need for a research project.
- Cite relevant literature sources to demonstrate state-of-the-art knowledge.
- Show your proficiency in the field by performing a critical evaluation of the subject while evaluating opposing points of view.
- Adding some references to your own previous work might help to demonstrate your expertise.
- Show how your project is relevant in the context of the current state of the art.

Since these are profound questions and you have very limited space, the background section is notoriously difficult to write.

This task is made even more complex because the answers to these questions might seem so obvious to you that you see no reason to include them. This is a psychological bias, known by the fitting name *The curse of knowledge*. In proposal writing *The curse of knowledge* can quickly turn into *The curse of rejection*.

The Background Card

To help you escape *The curse of knowledge* and create an effective outline for a background section that reviewers can easily follow, I created the *Research Project Background Card*. It consists of six sentences to which I provide the beginning and you have to fill in the rest. See the example Background card for the self-driving project to the right.

Writing these sentences out will make you step back, think about, and then convincingly express the reasons why the project needs to be completed post haste.

Once the card is filled in, the sentences will serve as guideposts for you to use when writing the full background section.

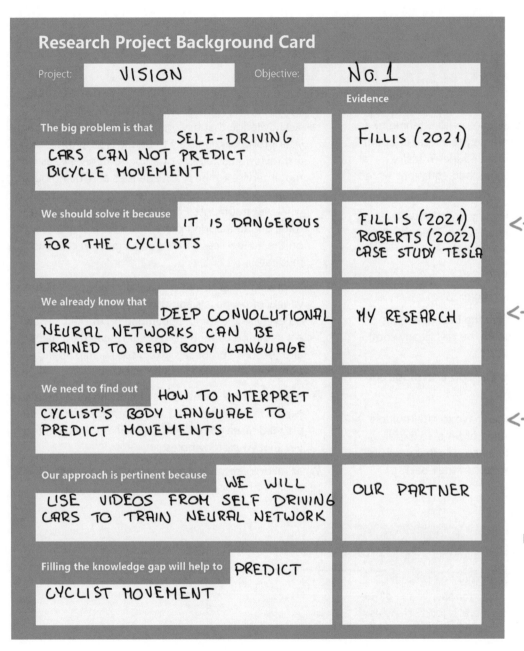

Research Project Background Card

Project: **VISION**   Objective: **No. 1**

Evidence

The big problem is that **SELF-DRIVING CARS CAN NOT PREDICT BICYCLE MOVEMENT** | **FILLIS (2021)**

We should solve it because **IT IS DANGEROUS FOR THE CYCLISTS** | **FILLIS (2021) ROBERTS (2022) CASE STUDY TESLA**

We already know that **DEEP CONVOLUTIONAL NEURAL NETWORKS CAN BE TRAINED TO READ BODY LANGUAGE** | **MY RESEARCH**

We need to find out **HOW TO INTERPRET CYCLIST'S BODY LANGUAGE TO PREDICT MOVEMENTS**

Our approach is pertinent because **WE WILL USE VIDEOS FROM SELF DRIVING CARS TO TRAIN NEURAL NETWORK** | **OUR PARTNER**

Filling the knowledge gap will help to **PREDICT CYCLIST MOVEMENT**

Write a separate background card for each knowledge gap

If you use your computer to fill in the card, use a reference manager to add citations in the evidence fields

You can provide evidence using references, preliminary data, a particular resource, or any other supporting material

The research objective in most cases is simply a rephrasing of this sentence

Download the
Background Card:
https://peerrecognized.com/
projectcanvas

Improve Readability

A while ago at a scientific conference I was listening to a presenter who delivered an extremely technical in-depth presentation. He was talking about Fourier Transformations, Finite Element simulations, and equations were flying all over his slides.

Since the subject was interesting, my gray matter was running on full power to try and keep up. Then the presenter advanced to a new slide and said:

Sorry, now it will get a little difficult.

Many people started to openly giggle.

While I am sure the presenter had the best intentions when he was delivering the speech, he was clearly another victim of the *Curse of Knowledge*.

When writing a proposal, try to **develop enormous empathy towards your reviewers**:

- Recognize that reviewers often have to rate multiple proposals in a very short period of time, so it is always in your best interest to make sure that your proposal is easy to follow regardless of their background.

- Acknowledge that having to weave their way through your proposal is unlikely to be the No.1 priority of any reviewer. Scientists often perform reviews as a moral service to the grant agencies and, being busy people, tend to squeeze the reading of proposals into whatever fragmented time slots they have - on the train, during a boring presentation at a conference, or on the hollow seat where people go to vacate and meditate.

- Appreciate that reviewers typically have to evaluate a variety of proposals and that they can not be experts on every single topic. Depending on the call, reviewers might be coming from other research domains, and for some proposals (like a scholarship application) they might not even be scientists.

- Assume that your reviewers are intelligent people and expect to be treated that way. Neither trivialize your planned research nor avoid explaining the complexities that your study holds.

What follows are several approaches for improving the readability of your proposal.

It's not just for proposals

The ability to see through complexity and present difficult concepts or issues in a simple manner is one of the main criteria that distinguishes merely good scientists from excellent ones.

Reduce unnecessary jargon

The sentence *Our research involves the GHF Sup-15-β perspiration on Dcav- at 4.36 DGY* is scientific gobbledygook. For that matter, the word *gobbledygook* itself is gobbledygook for many, apart from the most adept English language users. I should follow my own advice and use the word *jargon* instead, just to be sure that all my readers will know what I mean.

Scientists love jargon. And jargon works just fine for niche research papers that are only being read by other scientists interested in a narrow topic. Assume that your proposal will not be read by someone from the same niche, so make sure to write in a style and level of comprehension that is easy to follow.

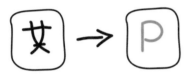

When you have to use gobbledygook, ahem... jargon, make sure to clearly explain what the terms mean in simpler terms. For example, after a necessarily complex sentence, you can follow up with one that summarizes the same thing in plain language.

Everything should be made as simple as possible, but not simpler.

I can not put it any better than that quote from Albert Einstein. What he meant was that it is important to express yourself in simple language, without *dumbing down* the complexities such that your ideas no longer have value.

Of course, using scientific terminology is not bad by itself. It demonstrates your expertise in the subject area, and for specialists it makes it easier and quicker to understand the text.

Unfortunately, there is no magic trick that will help you get through the conundrum of balancing your use of technical details with the simplicity of comprehension. Your best bet is to try to gauge the level of technical knowledge your reviewers might have and use language they will understand. In other words (and I have to repeat myself) - develop enormous empathy for your reviewers.

Read example proposals

A great way to improve grant-writing skills is to get inspired from the proposals of other scientists. On the webpage http://peerrecognized.com/projectcanvas you will find many **grant proposal examples** on various research topics. Just keep in mind that a grant approval does not always mean that the proposal was as good as it might need to be with stiffer competi-

Use active voice (mostly)

The Right Honorable gentleman from the Conservative party...

is the way that senior members of the British parliament have to be addressed during debates, even nowadays. This formal beginning of the sentence is sometimes followed with something along the lines of

...should stay in his seat and shut up.

The convention of addressing a person as *Right Honorable* is similar to the forced use of the *passive voice* in academic writing. Most often it is done only for the sake of tradition and its usefulness is questionable at best.

Is this your reflection in the mirror? No? Then consider using active voice.

Passive voice	Active voice
Machine learning will be used to process the data	*We will use machine learning to process the data*

The use of the passive voice – *what will be done* – makes the text sound more formal and impersonal compared to the active what *we will do*. This is the opposite of what you should aim for in a proposal.

In a proposal, you want to use a language style that highlights YOUR expertise, YOUR ideas, and YOUR plans. This subtle self-promotion using the active voice will work best if you reserve it for places where the reviewers should pay attention to your unique contribution. This might be during the explanation of the resources you have lined up, how you will execute the project, or how you will disseminate the results.

This is not to say that passive voice should be avoided altogether. The best proposals use a combination of passive and active voice. Here are two examples of where you could use passive voice:

1. When you want to emphasize the action instead of the doer, use the passive voice, such as when describing research methods (unless there is something unique about the method you are offering).

2. When it is clear who is performing the activity, or it is irrelevant to the discussion. For example, if you were to say:

Oceans are being polluted with plastic at an unprecedented rate.

It is clear who is causing the pollution so, if you want to put emphasis on oceans instead of humans, this sentence is absolutely fine.

REDUCE JARGON + USE ACTIVE VOICE = WRITE TO A FRIEND

It's tedious to keep reminding yourself to use active instead of passive voice and it is very annoying to have to continually rewrite text because there is too much jargon. So, it's best that you don't even think about it this way.

Implementing both of these pieces of advice will come naturally if, rather than treating the text as a research proposal, you think of it as a letter to a colleague or acquaintance of yours whose technical knowledge is at about the same level as what you expect the reviewers to be.

First think of a specific person that you know, like and respect. Now write in a way that will help that person learn a little more about the project you are proposing.

To help imprint this hack into your subconscious mind, start by addressing the recipient as you would in a personal letter (e.g. *Dear John*). (Just remember to delete this intro before submitting the proposal.)

The mindset of writing to a specific person should help you to write more clearly, provided you also use active voice and avoid jargon.

Here is an example from Aerin Jacob, a conservation scientist and adjunct professor at the University of Northern British Columbia. She remembers that in her early proposals she would make the text unnecessarily complex*:

> *I propose to study the heterogeneity of forest landscapes in spatial and temporal recovery after multiple disturbances*

rather than

> *I want to see what happens when a forest has been logged, burnt and farmed, and grows back.*

You have to agree that the rewritten sentence reads better and, unlike the original sentence, could be a part of a letter starting with *Dear John*.

*Sohn, Secrets to writing a winning grant. 2019, *Nature 577, 133–135*

Avoid a wall of text

Another pitfall facing research grant proposal writers is the sheer amount of information that scientists try to pack in. This is understandable and, to some extent, even necessary to fulfill the requirements of the grant agency. However, the proposal still needs to be easily consumable by the reviewers.

To avoid creating a wall of text, make judicious use of figures, tables, text boxes, bullet points, quotes, headings, and highlighting or other clarifying elements in your writing.

I religiously stick to my own advice on this technique. If you browse through the 374 pages I have written so far for the Peer Recognized book series, you will not find a single text-only opening. There will always be a content element that helps to split up the text.

This table shows how various content elements can be used in a proposal. —>

Notice how daunting the prospect of reading the dense wall of text on the left side of this figure seems compared to the one on the right.

Content element	Example use cases
Figures/graphics, images	• To explain concepts, methodology, proposal structure, test setup, etc. • Attract attention • Get imprinted on the memory of the reviewer
Tables	• Describe functions of researchers, risks, tasks, consortium, timeline, methods, dissemination, etc. • Connect the questions from the research call with the outcomes of your project
Highlighted text	• Use **bold**, <u>underlined</u>, *italic,* UPPERCASE, or differently colored text to highlight important statements which the reviewers should not miss. • Highlight a max 5% of text. Highlighting everything means that nothing is highlighted.
Bulleted or numbered lists	• List important items • Add tangible specifics to your proposal
Text boxes	• Explain important concepts of the proposal • Highlight any parts that answer the questions raised in the research call • Focus attention on key aspects of the proposal
Headings and subheadings	• Structure the proposal (often the main headings are defined in the research call guide or template) • Provide the ability to easily navigate the proposal to find relevant information • Don't use more than three top-level headings. Many sub-headings just show that your proposal is not well thought-through.
White space	• Add enough spacing between lines and paragraphs (line spacing along with font size are often defined in the funders guide for applicants) • White space makes the proposal easier to read and allows one to focus the reader's attention to the key parts

Let me tell you a secret. The content of the table above started off as a wall of text. Then, I thought it would be hypocritical to advise avoiding a wall of text using... a wall of text. So I turned the content into a table. The process not only served to make the text more readable, it also made me think about each item in more detail and devise a way to explain each point clearer and using fewer words. I think you will agree that the resulting table is clear and informative. Certainly, it takes up less space than the original block of text.

Watch your language

It can irritate, or worse - confuse - reviewers if you use different words to explain the same thing. For example, if you use *test result* in one sentence and *measurement* in the next, the reviewer might start to wonder if these are the same things or slightly different. A confused reviewer is not your friend.

Always use the same words and phrases when explaining the same thing.

To ease the burden of keeping a consistent vocabulary throughout the proposal, you could create your own glossary. You don't have to include it in the proposal (although you could if the terms are very specific), but having the commonly used terms written down will allow you to avoid confusion.

For example, after finishing the first version of one of my proposals I noticed that I had used the terms data *curation workflows, data curation*, and *data sharing system* interchangeably. I wrote down the term that I liked the most (*data curation system*) and read through the proposal again, making sure I only used that one term. Find and replace functions will help with this task.

I also did a search to make sure that the word *database* did not appear in the proposal more than strictly necessary. I did this because the research call explicitly stated that it would not support the creation of any databases. That's an example of avoiding negative trigger words.

Sprinkle the right keywords

For *top-down* research calls, it is important to reassure the reviewers that your proposed research coincides with the vision of the sponsoring agency. One way to do it is to sprinkle in supportive keywords from the research call document throughout the proposal.

Come up with an exciting title

The title is the ultimate summary of your proposal. Therefore, an intriguing, even a bit provocative, title that produces a fitting acronym will help to cement your proposal in the memory of the reviewer. For example:

CANVAS: Create a Novel Vision for Advancing Science

The title will also be the first piece of information that the program officer will use to assign reviewers, so make sure it is descriptive enough to get you into the most informed hands.

To come up with a good title, first create a list of keywords and short phrases that:
- Describe the problem you will address,
- Summarize the main idea of your proposal,
- Demonstrate the impact that your project will have.

Now, try mixing up different combinations of these words to come up with a title of no more than 10 words. **A good title** will not only show the field of research but it will be specific enough to your proposal that it can not be confused with any of the other proposals you will be competing with.

Come up with a list of at least five potential titles ranging from descriptive to snappy and exciting. Then you can ask your peers to help you choose the winner.

Creating an acronym from the title will allow you to use it throughout the text instead of vague phrases like *this project*. Using an acronym is an excellent way to keep reminding the reviewer which of the many proposals they are currently reading.

Keywords serve as an extension of the title and fulfill much the same purpose - assigning your proposal to the most appropriate reviewer or committee, as well as enabling people to find it in databases. Rather than duplicating words from the title, use some of the words from your initial list that did not make it into the title.

Supplementary Documents

In addition to the research proposal, the funder might require you to submit a number of supplementary documents, such as a cover letter, CV, research output, ethics statement, biographical sketch, support letters from stakeholders and, for career-related grants, a career plan or statement of purpose.

All too often authors don't pay much attention to these documents, but spend their time polishing their research proposal instead. This common flaw can work to your advantage.

After all, there is only so much that you can do after a certain point with writing the proposal. Any further edits are unlikely to greatly improve your chances of getting funded. That is because almost any proposal could be deemed worthy of funding after reaching a certain quality threshold. This is why supplementary documents are so important. They are your opportunity to stand out.

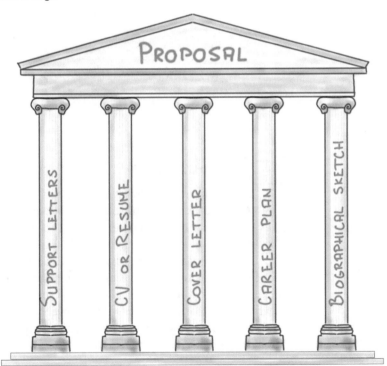

It's best to think of the additional documents as pillars which form a stable support structure for the proposal. Take one out, and your proposal might start to wobble.

Download **templates for the supplementary documents** from: https://peerrecognized.com/projectcanvas

Use these templates only if the funder does not provide their own.

95

CV or Resume

An academic CV (resume) lets the reviewers know about your formal training, work experience, skills, qualifications and what you have achieved in the past. Reviewers will use your CV to determine whether you are likely to deliver on what you promise in the proposal.

A list of publications, presentations, and grants might be a part of your CV unless a separate document is required.

Funders often provide a template or specify the sections of the CV you should include. If a template is not available, you can download my **CV template** from https://peerrecognized.com/projectcanvas. It includes the sections that typically make up an academic CV and a description of what to include in each.

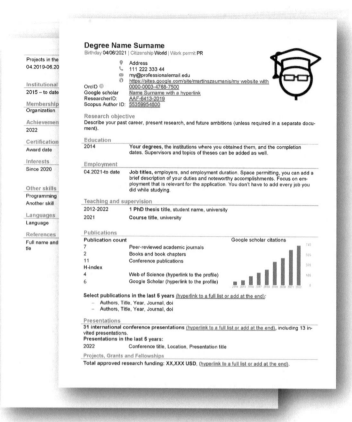

Be consistent

Make sure that the CV's of all project participants follow the same formatting style. Reviewers might assume that If you can not agree on such a simple thing as formatting, then- how can you be trusted to work as a team when you get the funding?

Tailor to audience

Structure your CV section content (most important first) according to two criteria:

1) Show that you have the qualifications needed for executing the project.

2) Show how your background matches the objectives and values of the funding organization.

Add hyperlinks

Including hyperlinks might help further convince the reviewers of your qualifications. For example, add links to your Google Scholar profile, ORCID profile, professional social media profile, your academic website, your research project web pages, any website that confirms you have received a certain award, and anything else that you feel might be relevant. Don't forget to add Digital Object Identifiers (DOIs) with hyperlinks to all of your research outputs.

Cover letter

Your cover letter is likely going to be the very first document that the administrator of the funding agency reviews. First and foremost, it will be used to evaluate whether your ideas align with the aims of the funder and then to determine which reviewers are assigned to your proposal.

Here is what you could include in your cover letter.

Description of the proposal

Briefly describe the key aspects of the proposal, including the problem the project will solve and the key scientific ideas.

Impact

Whether it's the funding agency, a private company, or your own university, they all have certain goals that they would like to achieve by funding you. Be sure to read the goals of the specific call and also browse the funder's website to find the their mission statement. Then, in the cover letter, show how your project will help them achieve these objectives.

Applicants

Identify the applicants (you and your team) and point out how your joint expertise will help to fulfill the project. This can be done on both a personal level and on an organizational level.

Personal motivation

A cover letter, unlike the proposal, is not a technical document. It's more like a conversation between you and the reviewers. Put aside the jargon and try to find a connection with the person reading it on a more human level.

Don't be afraid to reveal your personality and personal reasons for wanting to do the research.

 Download a **proposal cover letter** template:
https://peerrecognized.com/projectcanvas

Statement of Purpose (Career Plan)

A statement of purpose (also known as a career plan) is often required for career-related grants. This document can briefly touch upon your past career, but the emphasis should be on your medium and long-term scientific and academic career goals.

Aim to organize the document to answer these questions:

- **Career goal:** What do you want to achieve in your professional life?
- **Current work:** How will you build upon your previous work and skills to achieve your goals?
- **Research vision:** What problem do you want to work on? What questions do you want to answer?
- **Career plan:** How do you envision your career advancing in the future? What steps are you planning to take to achieve your future goals?

Career goal

In the first couple of sentences, state your ultimate career goal and briefly describe the steps you plan to take to get there.

Current work

In the next paragraph, aim to briefly (1-3 sentences) describe your current research and why it is important. What significant impact has it already had?

Your research record and past accomplishments are described at length in your CV or research output list, so you don't need to repeat them here unless something is particularly relevant to your future goals.

Rather, try to show how you will build on your current skills and acquire new ones in order to build a strong CV and achieve your career goals.

Research vision

In the following paragraphs you want to demonstrate a clear vision of how you expect your career to advance.

Action words for your career plan to help demonstrate your enthusiasm

Research	Leadership	Communication	Teaching	Organization	Creativity	Action
Proved	Handled	Influenced	Encouraged	Classified	Directed	Installed
Solved	Organized	Presented	Taught	Expanded	Shaped	Solved
Diagnosed	Coordinated	Interpreted	Trained	Accelerated	Published	Optimized
Interpreted	Oversaw	Lectured	Instructed	Generated	Integrated	Devised
Discovered	Planned	Edited	Coordinated	Unified	Founded	Programmed
Systematized	Analyzed	Collaborated	Explained	Tabulated	Visualized	Engineered
Modeled	Led	Wrote	Coached	Systematized	Created	Calculated
Resolved	Produced	Formulated	Advised	Structured	Invented	Standardized
Identified	Proved	Persuaded	Enabled	Changed	Developed	Built
Adapted	Consolidated	Directed	Stimulated	Simplified	Publicized	Computed

Although this is just speculation, it should not deter you from being specific. A murky vision signals a lack of focus to the reviewers.

Start by defining a big problem that keeps you up at night and how solving it will advance your field. Communicate how your future research will not only build on what you have done in the past but add new skills to your current expertise.

Now you can indicate the stepping stones that will take you closer to solving the big problem. The research gap you describe in the project proposal is but one of the stepping stones.

Show how the proposed research complements your quest to solve the big problem, but remember that your vision is what will drive you to continue working on a particular research direction even if you do not receive funding for your first ideas. Your drive is so great that you will simply regroup and try again.

Career plan

Envision how a successful career would ideally unfold for you and present this scenario in the document. Include activities like creating your own team, a description of your teaching priorities, the type of service work you want to do, collaborations you will foster, and other relevant professional activities (e.g. management, communication, supervision). Describe what steps you plan to take to fulfill these ambitions.

You could also include plans for mobility or applying for notable grants during, or after, the proposed project.

Statement of Purpose

Name Surname

What do you want to achieve in your professional life?
In the first couple of sentences, state your ultimate career goal and briefly describe the steps you plan to take to get there. Answer the question:

Current work

How will you build upon your previous work and skills to achieve your goals?
In the next paragraph, aim to briefly (1-3 sentences) describe your current research and why it is important. What significant impact has it already had?
Your research record and past accomplishments are described at length in your CV or research output list, so you don't need to repeat them here unless something is particularly relevant to your future goals. Rather, try to show how you will build on your current skills and acquire new ones in order to build a strong CV and achieve your career goals.

Focus area No.1: a specific research direction

What problem do you want to work on? What questions do you want to answer?
In the following paragraphs you want to demonstrate a clear vision of how you expect your career to advance. Although this is just speculation, it should not deter you from being specific. A murky vision signals a lack of focus to the reviewers.
Start by defining a big problem that keeps you up at night and how solving it will advance your field. Communicate how your future research will not only build on what you have done in the past but add new skills to your current expertise.
Now you can indicate the stepping stones that will take you closer to solving the big problem. The research gap you describe in the project proposal is but one of the stepping stones.
Show how the proposed research complements your quest to solve the big problem, but remember that your vision is what will drive you to continue working on a particular research direction even if you do not receive funding for your first ideas. Your drive is so great that you will simply regroup and try again.

You can include supportive figures that show research methodology or help organize the document. Don't be afraid to be original.

Career plan

How do you envision your career advancing in the future?
What steps are you planning to take to achieve your future goals?

Date, Location

Download **career plan template** from
https://peerrecognized.com/projectcanvas

Support letter

A support letter demonstrates that someone (e.g. supervisor, collaborator), or some entity (e.g. host university, stakeholder), has an interest in your research project, such that they may provide some form of support. Some agencies require, or at least allow, submission of support letters (also known as a letter of intent) while others don't, so find out before you prepare one.

A support letter:

- Shows that someone values your work.
- Specifies exactly how the collaborator will contribute to your research.
- Adds credibility when it comes from a respected collaborator.

Prepare the draft

Usually, as the proposal author, you will prepare a draft support letter that the collaborator will revise and sign. This approach is helpful for both parties:

- The collaborator will catch any unrealistic requests from your side.
- You will know what you can and can not expect from the collaborator.

Be specific

A support letter should be unique and contain specific details on how the collaborator will contribute to the project, including what roles and responsibilities the collaborator will have. Connect this contribution to the proposal by referring to specific tasks. This will show reviewers that you know how to organize a collaboration.

You should also briefly describe the background of the collaborator and explain why they are suited to contribute to your project. Here are some questions that will help you: *Do they have valuable expertise? Have they worked on a similar project in the past? Have you had*

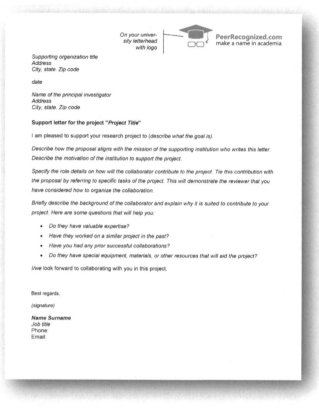

Download a **support letter template** with instructions for filling it from: https://peerrecognized.com/projectcanvas

any prior successful collaborations? Do they have special equipment, materials, or other resources that will aid the project?

Tie it all together

Refer to the contribution of the collaboration partner in your proposal text. This will show that their inclusion was not simply an afterthought.

A Proposal's Administrative Sections

This book and the Research Project Canvas are purposely focused on the scientific parts of a proposal. A proposal will, however, also contain aspects that are more administrative in nature, such as a risk mitigation plan, a data management plan, ethics and gender issues, management structure, etc.

Since the requirements for these parts are specific to the funding agency and change quite frequently, it is difficult to give general guidance. You can, however, seek out examples:

- Look up previous successful proposals for the same agency (make sure that the requirements have not changed). I will post links to example proposals on http://peerrecognized.com/projectcanvas but you can also use a search engine.

- Consult the grant administration office of your institution. There is usually someone in charge of helping scientists with proposals and they might have some examples for you.

- Ask for examples from your supervisor, colleagues, or project partners. Someone must have had a successful application. Sharing the administrative sections is not as big of a deal as sharing the scientific content.

- Look for instructions, instructional presentations and links on the research call submission guide, or on the website of the funding agency.

- Talk to the call's program officer and ask them for guidance.

- Get inspired by the examples provided on the

On https://peerrecognized.com/projectcanvas you will find examples of:
- **Project risk assessment table**
- **Data management plan**
- **Management structure description**

If you are willing to share the administrative parts of your successful proposals with other scientists, please send them to martins@peerrecognized.com. I will review them and upload to the book's webpage http://peerrecognized.com/projectcanvas.

Together we can develop a database of examples that will help you and fellow researchers focus on what you do best - perform research.

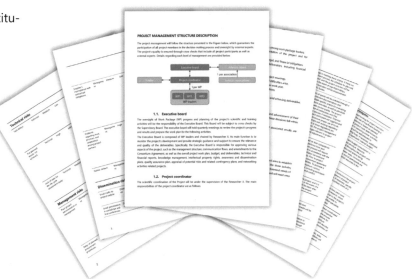

Edit, Edit, Edit

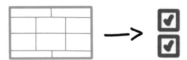

The researchers whose proposals get approved are not the best writers; they are the best editors. What I mean is that no one can write a perfect proposal in one go, so here are three ways to efficiently edit your proposal.

Ask a colleague to review it

Look for someone willing to provide *critical* feedback to your proposal. Finding a person who has both the time and the necessary expertise to perform such a task is not always easy. So once you find someone, hang on to them because generic feedback like *OMG, this is great!* might help your ego, but will do little to improve the proposal.

If you think that your proposal will be judged by experts outside of your field, try to find someone who is not familiar with your topic to do a review before submission.

To help you with editing, I created the *Proposal Review Checklist* (see next page). Following this checklist will enable you to perform a methodical review of different aspects of your proposal. Provide the Review Checklist to your confidant to make the review process more productive and facilitate discussion.

Take a break

It can be difficult to critique your own proposal. Being so deeply immersed in the ideas might prevent you from spotting obvious flaws.

An excellent treatment for this temporary blindness is to take time away from the proposal. A break will allow you to forget what you intended to write and read what is *actually* written. You will hopefully also break the emotional bond you acquired from all the work you put into writing the proposal. This should enable you to use the delete button more rigorously.

The length of the break depends on how much time you have before the deadline. My personal rule is to lock it away out of sight for at least one week. If the deadline is fast approaching, you could take a break from one part of the proposal in order to write other parts and then return to editing.

Read out loud

A highly underused editing tool is your own voice. Reading the proposal aloud will allow you to spot errors in logic, and you will stumble on sentences that are overly complicated or too long. Keep reading aloud and improving the text until you are satisfied.

Are your language skills insufficient? Try your best to improve them - it pays off not only through a better chance of receiving grants, having better language skills will even help you write clearer research papers. In the short term, though, paying a language editor to check the proposal might be a good investment.

On http://peerrecognized.com/projectcanvas you will find a list of **language proofreading tools** that will let you know if your text sounds too complex, highlight grammar mistakes, and remind you to avoid the using passive voice too often.

GENERATING → WRITING → *a Break* ↓ CONTENT → PROOFREADING → SUBMISSION DEADLINE
IDEAS   EDITING
← WEEKS TO MONTHS →

Research Proposal Review Checklist

Project: title   Designed by: name   Date: date

With helicopter-view editing you make sure that the proposal content is logical and covers all the key aspects

In the proofreading stage you make sure the text is easy to read and has no errors

Content editing
(do this while you still have time to revise)

Verify	What to improve
☐ The questions from the Research Projject Canvas are clearly answered	Comments
☐ Funding agency's requirements are followed and you have evaluated the proposal against the agency's review criteria	Comments
☐ The separate parts of the project are interconnected and bringing you closer to your objective (story structure is followed)	Comments
☐ The proposal follows logic and is well organized by paragraphs and section headings	Comments
☐ Enough evidence is provided to substantiate the claims and methodology	Comments
☐ Each figure conveys a clear message consistent with the text	Comments

Proofreading
(do this short before submission)

Verify	What to improve
☐ Sentences are clear and build on one another	Comments
☐ Grammar and spelling are error-free	Comments
☐ Consistent terminology is followed, keywords from the research call are used	Comments
☐ Jargon is used only where strictly necessary and any complex terminology is explained	Comments
☐ Content elements (text boxes, highlights, etc.) are used and there is enough white space	Comments
☐ The required formatting is used (incl. word count, headings, spacing, file naming, reference list, etc.)	Comments

Common Proposal Writing Mistakes

I was once a part of a proposal review committee consisting of five people. Every reviewer had listed the pros and cons for each of the eight proposals. After discussing the first proposal, we realized that we simply didn't have the time to discuss all of the pros so for the following proposals we settled only on discussing the drawbacks. To reach a consensus we evaluated each drawback against the criteria of the research call.

Unfortunately, it is sometimes not the power of the ideas that are included in the proposal that decides the outcome. In some cases, it is the absence of drawbacks that defines which proposals are approved.

Mistakes

Not considering evaluation criteria	Lacking focus	Failing to justify the research	Lacking clarity

Avoiding them

| Make the reviewer's job of finding flaws in your proposal difficult by ensuring that you have addressed each requirement clearly. Assess your own submission using the criteria reviewers have to follow. | Define a suitably narrow research question and stay focused on it. Don't diverge off on tangents and don't try to explain every minor methodology detail. Use the completed Project Canvas to stay on track. | Assume that reviewers don't know what the research question is. Explain the big picture, show where the pain lies and cite relevant sources that prove it. Use the Background card to start (see Part II) | Align the different parts of proposals (especially the problem, objectives, and methodology). Use the Project Canvas to ensure all important aspects are described. Show how your research will solve the identified problem. Note who will benefit from the results and how. |

Mistakes

Failing to submit on time	Cramming in too much text	Not following the required formatting guidelines	Not editing

Avoiding them

Besides writing the proposal, you might also be required to get approval from superiors, negotiate with partners, prepare CV's, collect support letters, plan the budget, and do many other things. Consider this and plan enough time for it. It is surprising how many scientists are one minute too late because they *did not anticipate that the server would be overloaded during the last few submission hours.*	White space helps with readability. Use tables, figures, bullet points, text boxes, highlight important phrases, and separate large text blocks with headings (see Part II).	The Research Project Canvas doesn't match the proposal structure of every funding agency. Make sure to follow the proposal structure according to the requirements of the funder and only use the Project Canvas as a guide. Check the call requirements for any required administrative details, formatting, and page count.	After preparing the first draft, set it aside for at least a week. Then thoroughly check it for logic and revise, revise, revise. Collect feedback from colleagues, partners, and supervisors and revise again. Use the *Review Checklist* (see Part II) and grammar checking tools. Finally, read the proposal out loud. This will help to ensure good readability.

Present the Proposal Orally

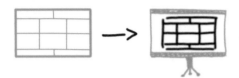

Sometimes you will need to pitch your proposal idea to a colleague to convince them to join your project. Or perhaps the funding agency will require you to present the proposal to a panel. And you will almost always have to explain the proposal to your supervisor. This means that you have to be ready to convincingly present the planned research.

Powerful presentations will not only help you win research projects. They will also generate interest in your research at scientific conferences, and enthuse your students during lectures.

*My book **Scientific Presentation Skills** will show you how to acquire academic presentation skills using the Five-S Pyramid. Get the book: https://peerrecognized.com/book3*

While I can not recite my entire book here, I will offer you a concise summary of some tips that I believe are crucial for successfully presenting a research proposal.

Elevator pitch formula

What would you say to them if you found yourself in an elevator with the person who could sponsor your next project? You would naturally deploy your *Elevator Pitch*.

Of course, elevators don't hold the exclusive rights to such short and focused presentations. You can use your pitch to convince your supervisor to support your research idea, or to persuade partners to join your team, or to present your project by the dinner table at a scientific conference.

Aim for a 30-second elevator pitch. This is a reasonable amount of time to hold their attention in a conversation.

An elevator pitch for a project typically answers four questions which, depending on the circumstances, may be followed by a call to action. See the *Elevator Pitch Formula* questions and the corresponding Project Canvas blocks below.

Here is an example elevator pitch for our self-driving car proposal. Notice that it is largely a condensed version of the Key Sentences

WHAT THE PROBLEM IS

HOW IT AFFECTS US

HOW I WILL WORK ON IT

WHAT THE SOLUTION WILL BE

+

CALL TO ACTION (OPTIONAL) → CALL TO ACTION

Self-driving cars have difficulties predicting the movement of cyclists, thus endangering this vulnerable traffic user group.

In the VISION project, we will first train a neural network to interpret a cyclist's body language in terms of their driving intentions. Then we will develop a code for real-time reaction based on the anticipated cyclist's movements.

The code will be open-access and car producers will be able to implement it for improving the safety of cyclists.

I would like to ask you to support the project by providing me with video footage from your car park.

On https://peerrecognized.com/ projectcanvas you will find the **Pitch Formula Worksheet.**

Decide on the focal points

When starting to prepare a full proposal presentation, think of what it is that you want to achieve with the talk. Now forget about it, because *no one cares about what you want.*

People most often just care about what you can do for them. In other words, you should develop deep and unconditional empathy for your listeners. Once you understand their wishes, you can try to tailor your message to fulfill them, while still reaching your own goals. If you can not determine how to fulfill the wishes of your audience, while simultaneously reaching your own goals, it might be the wrong audience

For example, a funding agency will only want to support a project that has a high chance of delivering noteworthy results, so your message might be:

> *My proposal includes a thorough methodology and I am the right person to lead the project.*

When you are talking to a potential research partner from the industry, one assumption might be that the company is interested in increasing its market share. Your message in this case might be:

> *The research results will bring you a competitive advantage.*

There can be countless other situations, so do your own analysis of your listener's wishes.

Browse through the Project Canvas blocks

After analyzing your audience, you can turn to the Research Project Canvas as a useful guide for preparing a presentation. Step into the shoes of your listeners and imagine which Project Canvas blocks they care about the most and which you can gloss over. For example, in a pitch to a potential industry partner, I would focus more on the results and the timeline and perhaps less on dissemination and resources. I would also dial down the nerdiness when explaining the methodology.

Two typical mistakes of proposal presentation

1. Assuming that the listeners know what the problem you want to solve is. Most often this assumption is wrong. Even in the rare cases when this is true, it is important to start by providing context so that your listeners know you are on the same page.

2. Not answering the *So what?* question. Researchers often get so carried away explaining methodology and the expected results, that they fail to explain why the results actually matter. Your listeners need to know the potential impact of your project, so make sure you clearly spell it out for them.

Prepare the presentation

Once you know the focal points of your presentation, you can turn to crafting its content. Of course, you could use the good old PowerPoint deck but consider using the Research Project Canvas for presenting.

The clear structure of the Project Canvas will allow the audience to easily follow your narrative. Demonstrating how the Canvas blocks are interconnected will show that you have considered the project holistically and thus the chances are high that you will reach your objectives.

Another advantage of using the Project Canvas for a presentation is that if the proposal is still in development, you can let your listeners know that this is just a draft. After the presentation, you can jointly improve the Project Canvas. Seeing that you are serious about their feedback will increase the chances that they will support you.

Different ways of using the Project Canvas in a presentation

Large print	Handouts	PowerPoint	Prezi
Print a large-sized copy of the Project Canvas and put it on the desk	Hand out a printout of a filled Project Canvas to everyone so they can follow along while you explain the content.	Show the Project Canvas in a *PowerPoint* slide and reveal details block by block. Add arrows to show connections between the blocks.	Use *Prezi* for panning through the Project Canvas and zoom into specific blocks to reveal details.

 Download **Prezi and PPT templates** for presenting using the Project Canvas: https://peerrecognized.com/projectcanvas

In a typical research proposal presentation, I would follow this sequence of presenting the Project Canvas blocks. But situations can differ, so make sure you tailor the presentation to your listeners

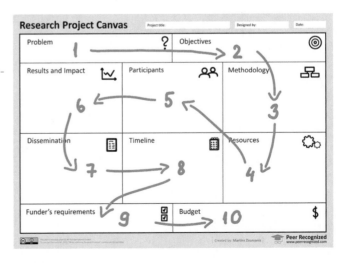

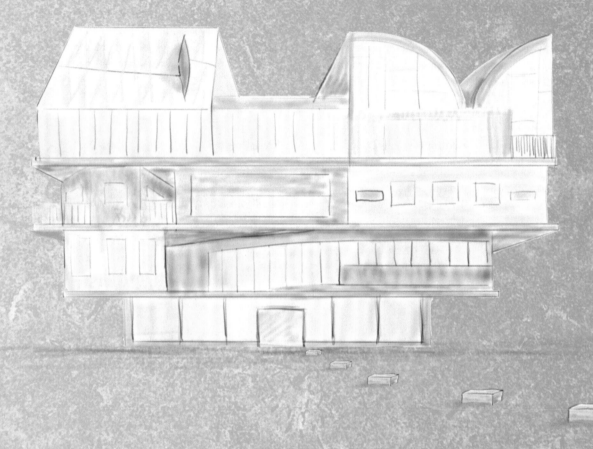

#PeerRecognized

GENERATE RESEARCH IDEAS

*D*addy, how can a fly walk upside down? Daddy, how do airplanes fly? Daddy, why is the sun shining?

I always take my daughter's questions as a challenge and then try to answer them in a scientifically sound way. And yes, I certainly attempt to find an age-appropriate language to explain nuclear fusion on the sun to my 4-year-old daughter.

Children are naturally wired to be curious. This innate curiosity about how things around us function is what drives scientists as well. Curiosity encourages us to ask questions and a well-formulated question is the first step to a research idea.

Unfortunately, curiosity often dissipates as we grow older and more complacent. While the education system is quite good at equipping us to answer questions and solve problems, rarely does any lecturer train students to be curious and ask meaningful questions.

Normally the professor gives you a task and provides a set of tools (physical or conceptual) to enable solving it. But it is not often that any professor would explain certain circumstances and ask the students to define what problem has to be solved.

Peter Drucker in his seminal book *The Landmarks of Tomorrow* introduced the term *Knowledge Worker*. He argued that knowledge work can not be broken down into a concrete workflow like at an assembly line in a car factory. It is simply not possible to specify the steps required for coming up with a great research idea. He is right but I believe it is possible to create an environment and cultivate personal habits that increase the likelihood of coming up with great ideas.

What time is it?

Einstein famously had the revelation about special relativity when he got curious looking at a clock tower in Bern, Switzerland. He thought* - *What would happen if I were to race away from the clock at the speed of light? My wristwatch would still continue ticking while the clock on the tower would seem to have stopped.*
The rest is, as they say, history (at least relatively speaking...).

*Isaacson, Einstein: His Life and Universe. 2008, *Simon & Schuster*

In the last part of this book, I want to equip you with some simple principles for designing an environment, both physical and conceptual, that will help you generate novel ideas and nurture your curiosity.

Please don't expect these tips to give you a world-changing research idea for the proposal you have to submit next week. Rather, consider them as slow-growth principles that will help you, given enough time, accumulate sufficient knowledge to one day spark an excellent research idea. The sooner you implement them, the faster that day will come.

If you do have an urgent deadline and desperately need to generate a research idea **RIGHT NOW**, skip to the end of this chapter. There I will equip you with some conceptual tools for facilitating the ideation process.

Where Good Ideas Come From

In the bestselling book *Where Good Ideas Come From* Steven Johnson argues that new ideas are generated in *the adjacent possible*.

> *Good ideas are not conjured out of thin air; they are built out of a collection of existing parts, the composition of which expands (and, occasionally, contracts) over time. Some of those parts are conceptual: ways of solving problems, or new definitions of what constitutes a problem in the first place. Some of them are, literally, mechanical parts.*

This notion is certainly not new. The entire academic environment is built around the principle of capitalizing on existing knowledge. This is why we share research results through scientific papers and exchange ideas at conferences. As academics, we stand on the shoulders of our predecessors.

Spelling out the concept of adjacent possible helps you to realize that coming up with good ideas first requires an extensive conceptual understanding of the subject you are researching, knowledge of the present scientific theories and the state of technological capabilities that limit what we can do in the current day and time. Then a scientist can arrange this knowledge in a way that stretches the sum of its parts a little further.

There is no single adjacent possible. Everyone's own consciousness sets the limit for how far their ideas can reach.

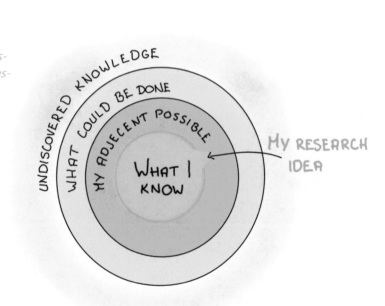

Expand Your Adjacent Possible

If you want to increase the chances of coming up with worthy new ideas, start by expanding your pool of knowledge. In this way, you will plant the seeds that can one day push into the adjacent possible of your scientific discipline.

Knowledge by itself, however, can not guarantee that you will generate great research ideas. Otherwise, the winners of quiz shows would also be the greatest innovators.

You also need to create an environment which can support the formation of new ideas using your acquired knowledge. The ideal environment includes physical components, such as research equipment and software, but it also includes the space around you that allows you to actively think.

Sound a bit abstract? Well, below is a list of specific elements that you can add to your daily habits to make sure that you create a fertile environment for generating new ideas. The list in this figure is certainly not exhaustive, but it's a good start from which you can borrow and tailor-make your own rituals. In this part of the book, we will progress through this list item by item.

NEW IDEAS

ACQUIRE NEW KNOWLEDGE
Read
Listen actively
Borrow from other fields
Write everything down
Learn new skills
Take up new hobbies

CULTIVATE CREATIVE ENVIRONMENT
Deliberately think
Go for a walk
Discuss
Cultivate healthy lifestyle
Make a sketch

Great research ideas are born at the intersection of knowledge and creativity.

Acquire New Knowledge

Being humble enough to admit we don't know things is a crucial job skill in science. We don't always have the answers and need to be willing to perform further research to create new knowledge.

Read a lot

Reading is an unsurpassed way of ingesting new information. Take time to read the latest research papers and note the future research directions which many authors add at the end of the papers and books. This might help you anticipate where your research domain is heading. Also be sure to read the classic books from the titans of your field as these will allow you to understand the ruling scientific paradigm of your science domain.

A single book or a journal article will probably not inspire a research idea, but given enough information, you will start to see connections between what needs to be done and what you could possibly do.

Make an effort to find reading time

Bill Gates takes a reading sabbatical every year. He reads in-depth books from fields where he is not a specialist. This allows him to merge the knowledge from different fields to come up with his own ideas.

Reading science books might not be everyone's idea of a perfect vacation, but do try to carve out time in your daily routine for reading scientific literature, both from within and outside your immediate specialty.

Listen actively

People tend not to listen during most conversations. Instead, they are waiting for their turn to speak. Try to break this habit. Active listening is not only more polite, it's a great way to acquire new knowledge and ideas, especially when talking with a knowledgeable peer.

People like it when others listen to what they have to say, so a useful side effect of active listening is that you become a more valued conversational partner. This, in turn, will give you even more opportunities for active listening.

Pay attention	Focus on your conversational partner rather than thinking about what you will say. Repeating key phrases and summarizing what the other person just said are good ways to show you are paying attention. Nodding and maintaining eye contact helps as well.
Ask in-depth questions	Ask clarifying and open-ended questions to ensure you understand. Questions also help you to steer the conversation in the direction that interests you.
Have an open mind	Withhold judgment and don't jump in with advice too quickly.
Allow for silence	Silence is a part of conversation. During engaging conversations, it simply means both of you are thinking.

Borrow from other fields

Taking ideas from other fields and applying them to yours is one of the fastest ways to come up with research-worthy topics. Perhaps there is a testing technique that you can borrow? Or a new material? Maybe an interesting technology?

Does borrowing ideas feel like cheating? Well, it isn't. In the book *Where Good Ideas Come From* Steven Johnson summarizes 134 most notable inventions from 1800 to present day. 88 of these inventions were born in teams where ideas were combined, built upon, and reimagined.

Merging ideas from different fields is, and has been, one of the primary ways scientists generate new knowledge. For example:

- Johannes Gutenberg developed the printing press by combining existing knowledge in the printing field (movable type, ink, paper) with the screw press that was used for winemaking.
- Pardis Sabeti combined her love of math with her expertise in genetics to analyze human evolution by using statistical methods. She is now a renowned professor at Harvard University having published multiple articles in Nature.

Different fields supplement each other

During World War II, engineers from the *Center for Naval Analyses* evaluated the damage to the planes returning from battle. They determined the typical places where planes were hit the most and recommended additional armor to better protect these areas.

A statistician then analyzed the same data and discovered that they had not considered that planes hit in the most critical areas would crash instead of returning. So in reality, the armor had to be added to the exact areas where the surviving planes had the least damage.

Write everything down

Once you have implemented at least some of the principles from before, you will generate a lot of new knowledge. At some point, the right connections will hopefully form between your brain neurons and trigger an idea. When this happens, it is vital to capture the idea even if it seems inconsequential at the time and you are not going to use it right away.

My personal preference is a searchable digital notebook because it is always with me and allows me to copy and paste text. If you like the analog feel of writing, a conventional notebook is also a perfectly good choice.

Either way, write down your ideas, along with any interesting quotes from research articles or books as well as the questions that you want to analyze.

The structure of the notebook is not as important as the act of writing itself. In fact, a somewhat messy notebook is likely to provoke more ideas due to the serendipitous connections it might trigger. Our brain has limited capacity for remembering, so a notebook will help you to return to your ideas later on and refine and connect them in ways you could not imagine at the time of writing them down.

The importance of accurate note taking

The psychobiologist Otto Loewi woke up in the middle of the night and jotted down some notes on a slip of thin paper before falling back to sleep.

The next morning he realized that he was unable to decipher the scribbling no matter how hard he tried. Fortunately, the same idea returned to him the next night. It ended up being the design of an experiment that proved chemical transmission of nerve impulses and earned him the 1936 Nobel prize.

Accurate notetaking matters.

Learn new research skills

To become the single best researcher in the world for any specific research specialization, you'd have to master it to perfection. This would take a lot of time and even then it is unlikely you'd succeed because there are so many researchers who are trying to do the same.

Below, in the figure that I adapted from Tomas Pueyo*, the vertical axis shows a person's proficiency at a particular skill and the horizontal axis displays the number of researchers who are good at it.

Observe what happens if, instead of trying to be the best in one particular skill, we add a second. The researcher no longer has to be the best at either of the two skills to be the best at the combination of the two.

To learn new research skills, you have to be willing to step outside your safe and familiar territory. Doing so is not easy because the brain chooses the path of least resistance by default; that is - it prefers to do what it knows how.

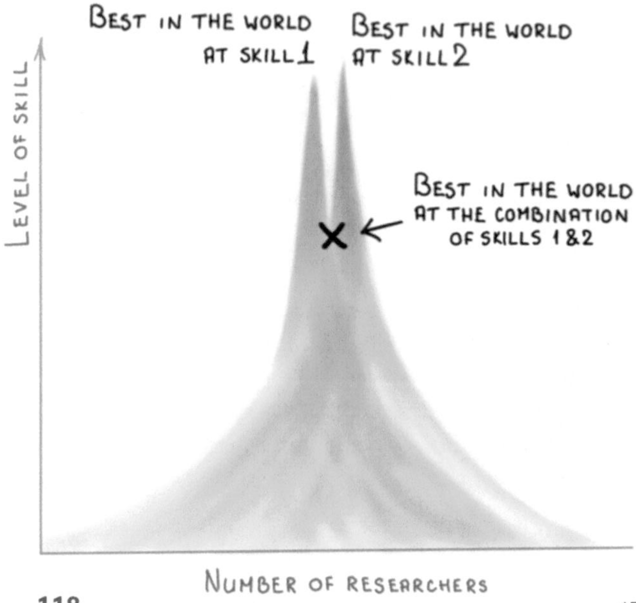

What to learn?

Exactly what you should learn about depends on how you want your career to develop. For example, I have taken up machine learning, even though I do not know anything about coding or artificial intelligence. I also do not intend to move to Silicon Valley, but learning a few things about this topic might just allow me to come up with new research ideas for my own field.

In case you can't think of a particular subject that you would like to take up, try returning to the basics and learn the foundations of some scientific domain other than what you already know. Once you start, it will probably invoke a deeper interest in a particular subject, which you can then explore in-depth.

Embrace ignorance

Learning something new requires a conscious effort and it is almost always frustrating at first because it requires stepping outside your comfort zone.

When I try to acquire a new skill, I already know that it will be difficult to understand how and why things work; I will easily get confused and overwhelmed; and sometimes I will get desperate and even feel stupid. But I always keep in mind that every new learner goes through this process and so I embrace the ignorance with open arms; I will try again and again to find ways to combine the new experiences with what I already know.

BEST IN THE WORLD AT SKILL 1

BEST IN THE WORLD AT SKILL 2

BEST IN THE WORLD AT THE COMBINATION OF SKILLS 1&2

LEVEL OF SKILL

NUMBER OF RESEARCHERS

Combine skills to come up with ideas that others would not be able to think of.

*Pueyo, How to Become the Best in the World at Something. 2019, *medium.com*

Specialization has a cost

To get to the edge of human knowledge in a specific field, you have to specialize. Rarely in any profession is this more true than in academia. It is, however, important to remember that specialization comes at a cost.

Nathan Myhrvold got his PhD in theoretical physics and performed his postdoctoral research in the group of Stephen Hawking. Bill Gates has called him the smartest person he knows. Here is what Myhrvold says about specialization*:

The world rewards specialization, but specialization comes at a cost. You learn more and more about less until you know everything about nothing.

Combine unique skills

One of the ways Myhrvold believes innovation works is by taking ideas from one place and applying them in a different context. He works on nuclear reactors, writes cookbooks, photographs wildlife, and does research in paleobiology and astronomy. This wide range of interests allows him to absorb new ideas and combine them with the knowledge he already possesses.

This can be nicely demonstrated with the figure we explored earlier. See what happens if we add a third skill in it, only this time imagine that the skill is very different from the first two, meaning it lands much further apart on the chart. Now only a few people in the world have this combination of skills.

If the skills are complementary to your profession, like No.1 and No.2 in the figure, you will still need to be among the best in the world at each particular one (say a computer programmer learning a new programming language). But if the new skill comes from a different field entirely (like a theoretical physicist writing a pizza cookbook) the chances are rare that anyone will possess this unique combination of skills.

HIGH OVERLAP BETWEEN THE SKILLS

LEVEL OF SKILL

BEST IN THE WORLD AT SKILL 1

BEST IN THE WORLD AT SKILL 2

BEST IN THE WORLD AT SKILL 3

BEST IN THE WORLD AT THE COMBINATION OF SKILLS 1 & 2

LITTLE OVERLAP BETWEEN THE SKILLS

BEST IN THE WORLD AT THE COMBINATION OF SKILLS 2 & 3

NUMBER OF RESEARCHERS

Combining distant skills lowers the barrier for becoming the world's best at something.

*The Creative Brain. 2019, *Netflix

Take up hobbies

I can just imagine the face of my boss if I were to ask his permission to write a cookbook during working hours, like Nathan Myhrvold does. You know, with the assurance that it will allow me to generate new research ideas.

So instead of asking my boss for a pizza oven, I put a lot of effort into choosing hobbies in a way that exposes me to new areas. I call them projects. Some projects last a couple of months, some can take years. But they are intentionally quite detached from what I do in research.

Over the years, I have learned how to create websites, draw, use image processing software and fix cars; I taught myself to play tennis and the principles of investing in the stock market; I learned the basics of building a business and established a football club for kids together with my friends. The *Peer Recognized* book series that you are reading was also born as one such project.

My hobbies over the years and the different ways in which they have inter-connected.

Connect the dots afterwards

Although my hobbies are quite diverse, they still find ways to create serendipitous connections and eventually some of them end up helping my research. For example, although my brief love affair with photography was unsuccessful, and left me with an expensive camera that I don't use, it still provided me with technical knowledge about light spectra which gave me an idea for how to quantitatively analyze microscopy images.

Naturally, the combination of rarely possessed skills will not always yield a great research idea. It might not help if a mathematician learns to knit (although perhaps this is how string theory was born?). But the chances are that eventually a unique set of multiple skills will morph into an innovative idea. In the words of Steve Jobs*:

> *You can't connect the dots looking forward; you can only connect them looking backwards. So you have to trust that the dots will somehow connect in your future. You have to trust in something — your gut, destiny, life, karma, whatever.*

The world is full of examples where researchers combined personal interests with their expert knowledge, yielding an extraordinary result:

- Leonardo da Vinci merged his expertise in painting with his interest in the human body to create some of the first anatomical drawings of the human body.
- Giles Bowkett used his proficiency in Ruby programming and combined it with his interest in producing dance music to develop Archaeopteryx (Archaeopteryx MIDI generator is an artificial intelligence software that writes and plays dance music).

*Stanford University Commencement Speech, 2005

Cultivate Creative Environment

In many scientific fields your work environment will include lab equipment that you dabble with but, in this section of the book, let's focus on the space around us that any scientist would find useful, regardless of their field of research.

Deliberately think

In episode 4 of the third season of The Big Bang Theory, a scene shows Sheldon and Raj solving a problem. They have written down some equations on a whiteboard and to the tune of *Eye of The Tiger* from *Rocky* they stare at it intensely. The focused thinking is only momentarily interrupted by Raj taking some aspirin to remedy his headache before the staring continues.

Think back on how often you've dedicated time solely for actively, uninterruptedly solving a problem. When you do it, is your phone, music, internet and email turned off? Do you have a chance to think without your colleagues interrupting you? And for how long do you do it?

Long stretches of deliberate thinking should be a part of a routine workday for any researcher.

Finding time to think

In the book *Deep Work* * Cal Newport highlights the many ways in which you can cultivate a deep dive into thinking, working, and problem-solving. The one piece of advice from his book that I have found to be most useful is to schedule blocks of at least 40 minutes for uninterrupted thinking. I have several such sessions set aside every day before lunch. In fact, my calendar has a perpetual entry titled *Deep Work* that runs from 7:30 am until noon with the following description when it is opened:

> *During the Deep Work hours I will try to avoid e-mail, meetings, etc. I might also be working somewhere else instead of my office.*

Occasionally people still come by during these hours and I don't refuse a chat. But whenever someone wants to set up a meeting with me, they will most likely choose afternoon because my calendar already has a morning entry.

	MONDAY	TUESDAY	WEDNESDAY	THURSDAY	FRIDAY
	15	16	17	18	19
	Deep work	Deep work	Deep work	Deep work	Deep work
8 AM					
9					
10					
11					

* Cal Newport, Deep Work: Rules for Focused Success in a Distracted World, 2016, *Orell Fuessli*

Go for a walk

One's work environment can have many distractions. Computer screens, e-mails, phone messages, colleagues, and work obligations can kill a great research idea before it is even born.

Walking is a surprisingly simple and effective way to create an environment where none of those distractions exist and you can dive deep into your thoughts.

The best walking paths for thinking are slightly boring - busy streets or wonderful hikes on a mountain ridge will create distractions of their own. A good approach is to incorporate walking into your daily commute. For example, walking to work or taking a stroll to a distant grocery shop. Using the same boring route over and over again will better ensure you can focus on thinking.

Before heading out, select a topic you want to think about and do not let your mind wander away. Biologist Charles Darwin, mathematician Henri Poincare, and computer scientist Cal Newport are just a few of the famous academics who incorporated walking into their routine.

An alternative strategy to active thinking during the walk is to let your brain mindlessly wander. Counter-intuitively, this might even be more productive than forcing yourself to think about something specific. The mind needs time during a period of slight boredom to create new serendipitous connections between brain cells.

Of course, walking doesn't have the exclusive rights for generating ideas. Soaking in a bathtub, commuting in a car, flying, or stretching are some other options for uninterrupted thinking. But overall, walking seems to be the easiest way to achieve solitude, simply because it can be done anywhere and at almost any time. In today's attention-grabbing world, the ability to leave technology behind and be alone with your thoughts is more difficult than it sounds.

Engage in scientific discussions

Many of the world's greatest discoveries are the result of fruitful collaborations between researchers. Tough questions and challenging inquiries from knowledgeable conversation partners help to define problems as well as find ways of solving them. The very act of explaining a certain topic can, by itself, help to clarify a problem and come up with potential solutions. Whether it is through setting up meetings with colleagues, or just hanging out by the coffee machine, try to find ways to engage in potentially fruitful scientific discussions.

For example, Jennifer Doudna and Emmanuelle Charpentier met at a conference in the spring of 2011 and started working together on genome editing using CRISPR/Cas9. During the most intense period of data analysis and manuscript writing, Doudna was in the U.S. while Charpentier was in Sweden. Due to the time difference, one would work while the other was sleeping. They would have intense daily exchanges. The collaboration resulted in a 2012 landmark paper* which eventually earned them a Nobel prize in 2020.

Even Albert Einstein and Thomas Edison, despite popular legends, were also not lone-wolf geniuses:

- Einstein received a lot of help from mathematician Marcel Grossmann who expressed Einstein's abstract theories in elegant equations. He also engaged in fruitful discussions with the engineer Michele Besso.
- Edison, despite the popular credit for being the sole inventor of the lightbulb, actually learned a lot through competition with his rivals. Multiple people contributed crucial pieces of the puzzle which eventually brought light to every home.

In the book Where Good Ideas Come From Steven Johnson lists 135 of the most important innovations during the last two centuries. Two-thirds of the ideas were born through collaborations and only one third was generated by a scientist working in solitude.

Jinek et. al, A programmable dual-RNA-guided DNA endonuclease in adaptive bacterial immunity. 2012, *Science, 337(6096), 816–821.*

Make a sketch

Sketching a research plan, drawing a new test setup, or visualizing any other idea will force you to give shape to the early hunch that is just starting to form in your head. Sketching forces you to explicitly identify the different parts of an idea and provide connections between individual pieces to see the big picture. The process might not be easy at first, but that is the whole point. Sketching will force your brain to actively think about and then lay out specifics about whatever subject you are trying to materialize.

Avoid using graphic software (e.g. *PowerPoint*) in this process. You have to be able to scribble, erase, redraw, create better versions, and throw the bad ones in the paper basket with ease. Using software will create unnecessary difficulties in quickly visualizing your thoughts.

I like sketching on a piece of paper, but occasionally I also use my tablet with a stylus, or a whiteboard. The medium doesn't matter as much as the intimate connection between you and your ideas.

It also doesn't matter how ugly the sketches look. These are not meant for sharing with others. Well... unless you decide to write a book and include them as examples, like what I am doing here.

Cultivate healthy lifestyle

Healthy regular meals, physical exercise, enough sleep, and time away from work are the basics of a healthy lifestyle. I will not try to convince you to live like a monk, but I do want to remind you that the brain is a scientist's main tool. It is a bad craftsman who does not take care of his main tool.

I enjoy books about the history of science and have noticed that one aspect of a healthy lifestyle repeated itself in different situations. Sleep.

Although scientists only vaguely understand how the brain works, it seems that at night our subconscious mind keeps working on problems that are implanted in our brain at daytime. During sleep, new connections are formed between parts of the brain that don't normally connect during waking hours. It is no wonder that many scientists claim that the breakthroughs to their discoveries came in the form of dreams:

- Dmitri Mendeleyev dreamt of the layout for the periodic table.
- Alfred Russel Wallace had an epiphany for the theory of natural selection in his sleep.
- Niels Bohr dreamt the structure of the atom.

Even if new ideas do not rush into your mind at night, a good sleep will still allow you to focus better during your waking hours. By a good night's sleep, I mean following a certain schedule, letting the mind relax, not watching movies until late evening and not checking phone messages while you are still half-awake.

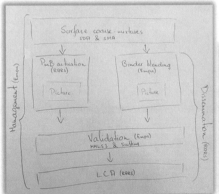

Generate Research Ideas Right Now

GENERATING IDEAS

What if you don't have the time to learn new skills, or wait for an epiphany to visit you during your sleep? What if you need an idea RIGHT NOW!?

There prompts will help you quickly come up with new ideas.

Canvas Block	Prompts
Problem	What problem needs to be solved? What are some knowledge gaps which authors have identified in their research papers/books? What issues are being discussed at industry conferences? What obstacles am I facing during my own research? What observations are lacking theoretical background? What problems have my colleagues identified? (ask them) What problems are stakeholders facing? (ask them)
Objective	What research products need to be developed? What are the smaller steps that will help to solve a larger problem? What are some of the newer trends in my field?
Methodology	What methodology have I developed and could expand? What methodology needs improvement? What previous project could I build on? What hypothesis needs to be proven?
Resources	What could I accomplish by borrowing methods, technology, materials, or equipment from other fields? What could I do with the unique equipment I have? What could I do with the special materials I have? How could I make further use of my existing data?

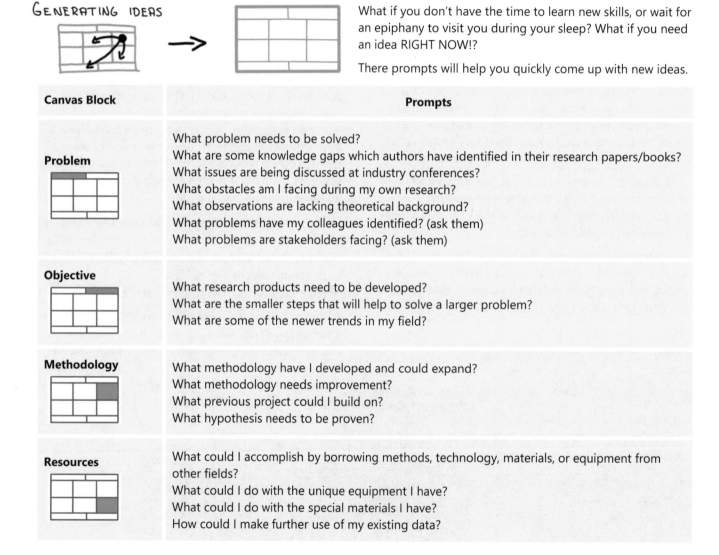

Participants	What am I good at/known for?
	What topics excite me?
	What unique skill-set do I possess?
	What problem could my partners help me solve?
	What intriguing problems do I want to solve during my career?

Results and Impact	What results are needed to solve a certain problem?
	What information is missing in my field?
	What needs to change?
	What could I do to make a real impact?

Dissemination	What results need to be shared?
	What intellectual property needs to be protected?
	How can I improve the communication of my scientific results?
	What or who could help me to share my results?

Timeline	What needs to be urgently solved?
	In what sequence should the identified research gap be filled?
	What can I manage to solve before I need to finish (e.g. moving to another institution or grant running out)?
	What are my competitors rushing to solve?

Funder's requirements	What topics are being requested in research call proposals?
	What problems are industry partners asking me to solve?
	What research is someone willing to pay me for?

Budget	What would I research if money were not an issue?
	What problem could I solve if I was able to buy some new device?
	What problem could I solve if only I could outsource the needed expertise?

Idea generation workflow

Step 1: Generate New Ideas

I have summarized the idea generation prompts in a *Research Idea Generator Worksheet.*

Be bold and write down everything that comes into your mind into the *My ideas* blocks. Don't prejudge yourself and feel free to write even the craziest ideas. The objective of brainstorming is not instant perfection.

 Download the **Idea Generator worksheet** at:http://peerrecognized.com/projectcanvas

Step 2: Sort through the ideas

Once you have generated many ideas, you can sort through them. Head back to the Research Project Canvas for this step. Start by filling in the block where the idea originated. Then fill the next blocks in the order of importance.

The sequence of filling in blocks will depend on the circumstances. As you go through the blocks and answer the questions contained within, the research proposal will become ever more clear in your head. You will also quickly realize if it is not possible to realize a particular idea at this time.

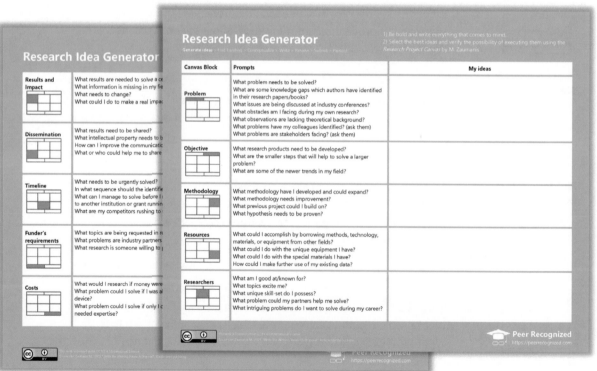

Here are some hypothetical examples for the inception of a proposal along with the three first blocks that an author might fill.

PROBLEM-DRIVEN

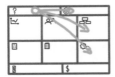

In the classic tale, a researcher identifies a real-world problem and then devises a research plan that will bring him/her one step closer to solving it. In this scenario you start with the *Problem* block, advance to *Objective* then to the required *Resources* and continue until you have filled all the blocks.

SPONSOR-DRIVEN

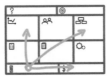

Often a government agency issues a research call on a specific topic and sets various requirements, like the budget, type of partnerships, and the maximum duration. In such a scenario, start to fill the Project Canvas from the *Requirements* block, then advance to devise a *Methodology* that will allow you to reach the expected *Results* and make the agency happy.

RESOURCE-DRIVEN

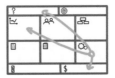

Imagine you have access to a new piece of equipment that no one else in your research domain has. Your best strategy would be to define a topic around that piece because it will allow you to produce unique results. For example, if you have access to the Large Hadron Collider, you had better be framing your project around it.

RESULT-DRIVEN

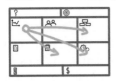

Should a company approach you to find a chemical they can use in production, start with the *Results* block. Then work backwards to identify the *Methodology* and *Resources* that will allow you to accomplish the task within the *Timeline* required by the company.

PARTNERSHIP-DRIVEN

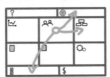

If you have a great collaboration partner at another university, you might try to find a project that will allow you to join forces. In this case, you would look for a *Funder* that supports collaborative projects. Then you'd define an *Objective* and work out a *Methodology* that allows you to build on each others' strengths.

IDEA-DRIVEN

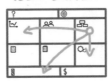

Imagine if, in the middle of the night, you came up with a great methodology that would allow everyone to better understand a certain aspect of the world around us. Now that you have an idea at hand you need to make sure you have the *Resources* and a *Funder* to realize it. You also need to define why your idea is important; that is - what *Results* does it promise.

NECESSITY-DRIVEN

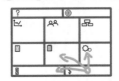

If you need to buy a piece of equipment, start with the *Budget* block. Then find a fitting *Funder* who will allow you to obtain the necessary funding in the required *Timeline* before even thinking about the other blocks.

Which Ideas to Pursue?

How do you best find the balance between passion and obligations? How do you decide which ideas to invest your time and energy on?

The answer to these questions is as simple as it is complicated - pursue the research ideas that interest you. Being motivated is important, primarily because achieving success in research relies as much on dedication and willingness to put in the extra hours as it does on any expertise and available equipment.

In the real world, however, you may need to adapt your ideas to the topics the funding agency wants to fund, or to the topics your students want to engage in, or because your employer requires you to bring in certain funding regardless of where your passion lies.

There will also be times when you have to decide between multiple project ideas. For example, you might be invited to participate in multiple consortia while also working on your own ideas

Any idea you decide to pursue will define how you spend your next months or even years. You have the opportunity to establish a professional expertise around the topic. If peers find it interesting, you will gather citations, collaboration opportunities will open up, and your prospects in the job market will rise. In other words, strategically selecting a research topic is one of the most important choices a scientist can encounter, all because the consequences will follow you for a long time.

Making use of the Research Project Canvas will help you to sieve your ideas and ultimately select those with the highest potential to bear fruit. There are, however, considerations apart from the likelihood of success that you might wish to consider.

Follow the money

Investment icon and television celebrity Kevin O'Leary often offers aspiring entrepreneurs on Shark Tank (a popular TV show about investing) the same advice: *Follow the money.*

This might seem a counterintuitive suggestion for an altruistic researcher who fights for a better world and a noble cause; some might even view the saying as sinister in the context of research. But, please, hear me out.

Reason 1: Words are cheap

Following the research money will not make you rich. You are probably already aware that there are much better ways to land on the cover of *Forbes* than by being a researcher.

Instead, the somewhat philosophical reason to follow the money is that funding offers a (mostly) neutral judgment of worth, and research is not an exception.

Complimentary words are cheap. People tend to flatter others because they want to avoid conflict. But if someone is actually willing to pay for a research project, it serves as a better indicator of value.

Reason 2: Learn to adapt

The principle of following the money means that you should not wait for the one perfect research call where you will deploy your one and only ingenious idea. Especially if you are a young scientist, you should be ready to adapt and make the best out of what is possible at a particular time and place.

Actively looking for, and pivoting, your ideas depending on the requirements of the funder will almost certainly yield more results than waiting for that one perfect opportunity. Besides, no matter what happens, you will gather proposal writing experience so that you are better prepared when the right moment comes.

Reason 3: Secure resources

Securing funding will also ensure that you can maintain your own wage, buy equipment, hire help, and travel to conferences to meet other people. All of these benefits will contribute to generating new research ideas and improving your research skills. Importantly, the ability to bring in funding is a well appreciated quality for a young scientist. It will help you to earn the approval of your supervisor and increase your chances of success when you apply for larger grants later on.

Not least importantly, secured funding will allow you to live an overall happier life and provide time for engaging in activities outside of work. No matter how much you romanticize the profession of scientist, you are still a human being with needs outside the lab. Living a more fulfilled life will probably also enable you to become a better researcher.

Integrity

Please do not confuse my advice to follow the money with doing whatever it takes to acquire funding. In no scenario should you ever compromise your integrity, regardless of who is sponsoring your project or for what purpose. Integrity is the greatest asset a scientist has and without it, your academic career will be short-lived.

Gauging the ambition level

If you propose something mundane the reviewer will think it's not ambitious enough; submit a proposal that flies too high in the sky and no one will believe that it's possible to achieve what it promises. You can trust me on this, as I've been rejected for both reasons.

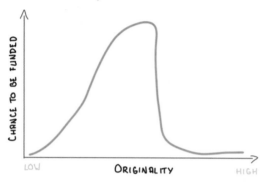

Unfortunately there is no simple formula for how to gauge the sweet spot, so don't take the following advice as gospel. Rather, view them as principles that you can consider when making your own judgment.

Judge the funder's expectations

First of all, judge the type of funding you are applying for (the Funders Requirement's block in the Project Canvas). Some grants are intended for projects that are at a high technology readiness level and the grant agency will expect the results to bring tangible benefit in the near future. Other funding instruments might be intended for highly ambitious or transformative research that brings fundamentally new understanding to a particular subject, even if there is no immediate use for such knowledge.

Before even starting to write, gather enough information to make a clear judgment of the ambition level that is expected by the funder. The holy submission guide, the funder's website, reports of previous grant proposals,

proposal abstracts, the program officer, and your colleagues are the most likely sources of this information.

Start small

The reviewers will judge your level of experience and grant funding only to proposals that have a realistic chance of being successfully completed. A multi-year project for a radical new research direction led by a recent PhD graduate will likely return a review comment stating that the proposed work is too ambitious, no matter how well the proposal is written.

It is very important for a young scientist to have original and ambitious research ideas and, if you have the courage, you can certainly write such a proposal. The risk is that after a couple of failures you run out of funding and become jobless.

For this reason, submitting a less ambitious proposal which has a realistic chance of delivering useful results might sometimes be a better career choice. A funded proposal, albeit not groundbreaking, will ensure you live to research another day: you will have a job and you will produce results that you can publish. Every successfully completed project will increase your chances of securing more ambitious projects in the future.

*Chart based on the figure in Schachman H.K. (2006), From "Publish of Perish" to "Patent and Prosper", J. of Biological Chemistry: 281,11

Ask really big questions

Once you have a strong CV, and a proven record of successfully managing research projects, you can raise your ambitions. You are ready to ask the really big questions which have the potential to make a significant impact on your research field and beyond it.

Deploy exploratory studies

Before attempting breakthrough research it is often a good idea to deploy exploratory studies. Even if you have a world-changing idea that just has to be funded, start with the first step.

Put in some extra hours in the evenings, or motivate a student to select your idea as a research topic. You want to prove the concept works and make sure that you can reasonably expect to deliver on the promises made in a full research proposal. You can even use the results from such exploratory studies to strengthen your project proposal. Reviewers always appreciate evidence, even if it is not published yet.

Another way to increase the chances of getting to work on a highly ambitious idea is to include it as a small part of a larger proposal. If the ambitious part fails, you will still deliver results for the bulk of the proposal. Should the side study show promising results, you might be able to negotiate a change of objectives with the funder.

Research projects are often forced to change direction so this should not come as a surprise to the program administrator. Most often changes are implemented because the proposed research plan did not keep up with the promises. By offering to deliver more remarkable results than originally proposed, you might even pleasantly surprise the funders.

Finally, even if you do not change the course of the given project, you can capitalize on the ambitious part of the research project by writing publications and proposing a new project that specifically focuses on the ambitious topic. Then your chances of being funded will be higher because of your prior success in the subject.

Inviting a star professor

It can be tempting to invite a star professor to join in on your proposal since the recognizable name might impress the reviewers and the person could provide good advice on writing the proposal.

It might seem like an opportunity, but be cautious. The star professor could see your invite as a free lottery ticket: no harm in joining since they don't have to do anything, while having a small chance at getting funding. In such a situation, it's possible that the only help you will get in writing the proposal is a comment similar to: *I do not understand this, please rewrite.*

If you go this route, just make sure to agree on the commitment from the collaborator before joining forces.

Compete with scientists in the same career stage

If you are an early-stage researcher, check if the grant agency you are considering offers grants specifically for this group. If they do, your competition would be other scientists at a similar career stage.

Rate Your Research Ideas

RATING IDEAS ★★★☆☆

You will probably be able to generate more than one Project Canvas with an idea worthy of pursuing. With several in hand, you need to judge their potential. This is the time when you need to look in the mirror and honestly admit to yourself that there is no shortage of ideas in the research world and there are a vast number of open questions that need to be answered.

You therefore need to focus on the best ideas which have the greatest potential for impact. You also should make sure that you have everything needed to execute your project. Using the Research Project Canvas will help you to find answers to these questions.

As you rate your ideas, be brutally honest with yourself and discard any ideas that do not hold enough potential. Time is a nonrenewable resource and it is simply not worth investing in writing grant applications that have little chance of being funded or delivering the results that you aim for.

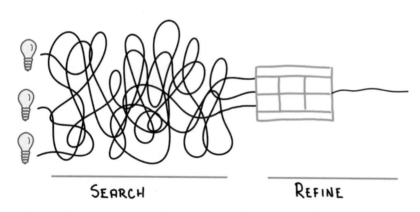

SEARCH   REFINE

When evaluating proposals for public funding agencies, reviewers are required to use a defined set of criteria. The criteria are always published on the funder's webpage. Use the defined criteria, along with the Research Project Canvas to refine your proposal.

To judge and compare research ideas at an early stage, use the *Research Proposal Scorecard*. Use it to methodically rate your ideas and write down the main reasons for scoring the way you did on the Scorecard so that you can recall your rationale later on.

Once done, staple the Scorecard together with the respective Project Canvas. If at some point the circumstances change, you will be able to come back to the Project Canvas and modify your ratings.

Download the **Research Proposal Scorecard** from http://peerrecognized.com/projectcanvas

Research Proposal Scorecard

Project:	title	Designed by:	name	Date	date

Research Project Canvas Block	Weak	Score	Strong	Comments
Problem	The problem is vaguely defined or does not fit the goals of the funder.	-3 -2 -1 0 +1 +2 +3 ☐ ☐ ☐ ☐ ☐ ☐ ☐	The project addresses an urgent problem and a clear research gap is identified.	Why did you give this rating?
Objective	The objectives are too complex, unclear, or unrealistic.	-3 -2 -1 0 +1 +2 +3 ☐ ☐ ☐ ☐ ☐ ☐ ☐	The objective is Specific, Measurable, Ambitious, Realistic, and Time-bound (SMART).	Why did you give this rating?
Methodology	The methodology is ambiguous or the effort is not well balanced between the individual project's parts.	-3 -2 -1 0 +1 +2 +3 ☐ ☐ ☐ ☐ ☐ ☐ ☐	The core methodology of the project is relevant and clearly explained.	Why did you give this rating?
Resources	The availability of the necessary resources during the project is unclear.	-3 -2 -1 0 +1 +2 +3 ☐ ☐ ☐ ☐ ☐ ☐ ☐	The necessary resources (research facilities/data/co-funding/preliminary findings, etc.) are available and their use will allow applying the planned methodology.	Why did you give this rating?
Research team	The researchers are lacking appropriate background and have not had successful collaborations.	-3 -2 -1 0 +1 +2 +3 ☐ ☐ ☐ ☐ ☐ ☐ ☐	The research team has relevant experience, the roles are clearly defined and they have previous collaborations.	Why did you give this rating?
Results and Impact	It is unclear what knowledge will be generated and what impact the results will have.	-3 -2 -1 0 +1 +2 +3 ☐ ☐ ☐ ☐ ☐ ☐ ☐	The anticipated results are identified and pertinent to the defined knowledge gap. It is clear who benefits from the work and in what way.	Why did you give this rating?
Dissemination	Dissemination does not include relevant channels for reaching the target groups.	-3 -2 -1 0 +1 +2 +3 ☐ ☐ ☐ ☐ ☐ ☐ ☐	Dissemination activities are proportional to the ambition of the project and tailored to the relevant audiences.	Why did you give this rating?
Timeline	The timeline is confusing, overly ambitious, or contains critical dependencies.	-3 -2 -1 0 +1 +2 +3 ☐ ☐ ☐ ☐ ☐ ☐ ☐	The time spent on each activity is proportional to its complexity, the activities are well coordinated, and any boundary conditions are fulfilled.	Why did you give this rating?
Funder's requirements	It's unclear who will pay for the project and the funder's requirements are not known.	-3 -2 -1 0 +1 +2 +3 ☐ ☐ ☐ ☐ ☐ ☐ ☐	The likely funder is known, the planned budget is appropriate and the funder's requirements can be fulfilled.	Why did you give this rating?
Costs	The cost structure is ambiguous and not well balanced between tasks/partners.	-3 -2 -1 0 +1 +2 +3 ☐ ☐ ☐ ☐ ☐ ☐ ☐	The costs are clearly substantiated and proportional to the effort.	Why did you give this rating?

Total score (count the points):

Proposal Writing

The Research Project Canvas is the centerpiece of the approach I propose you use for coming up with a well-rounded research grant idea.

Besides the Proposal Canvas, I equipped you with many different templates and proposal writing tools. They will help you on every step to acquiring research funding, starting from generating grant ideas all the way through finding partners, writing the proposal, creating graphics, preparing supplementary documents, and finally submitting the best possible version of your idea.

Here is the workflow you can follow when preparing a proposal. Depending on the call requirements and how much time you have, you may need to adapt the items or perform them in parallel.

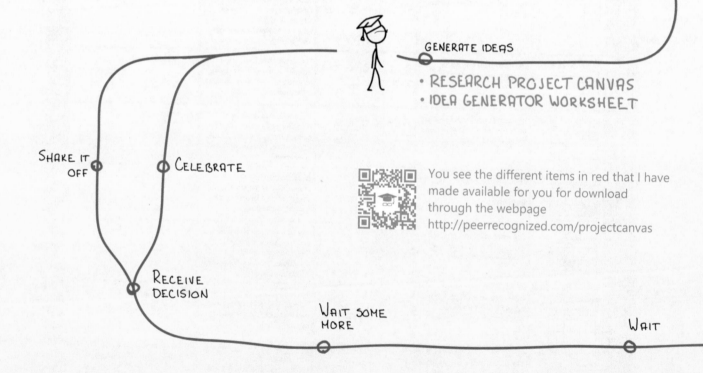

GENERATE IDEAS

- RESEARCH PROJECT CANVAS
- IDEA GENERATOR WORKSHEET

SHAKE IT OFF

CELEBRATE

RECEIVE DECISION

WAIT SOME MORE

WAIT

You see the different items in red that I have made available for you for download through the webpage
http://peerrecognized.com/projectcanvas

Workflow

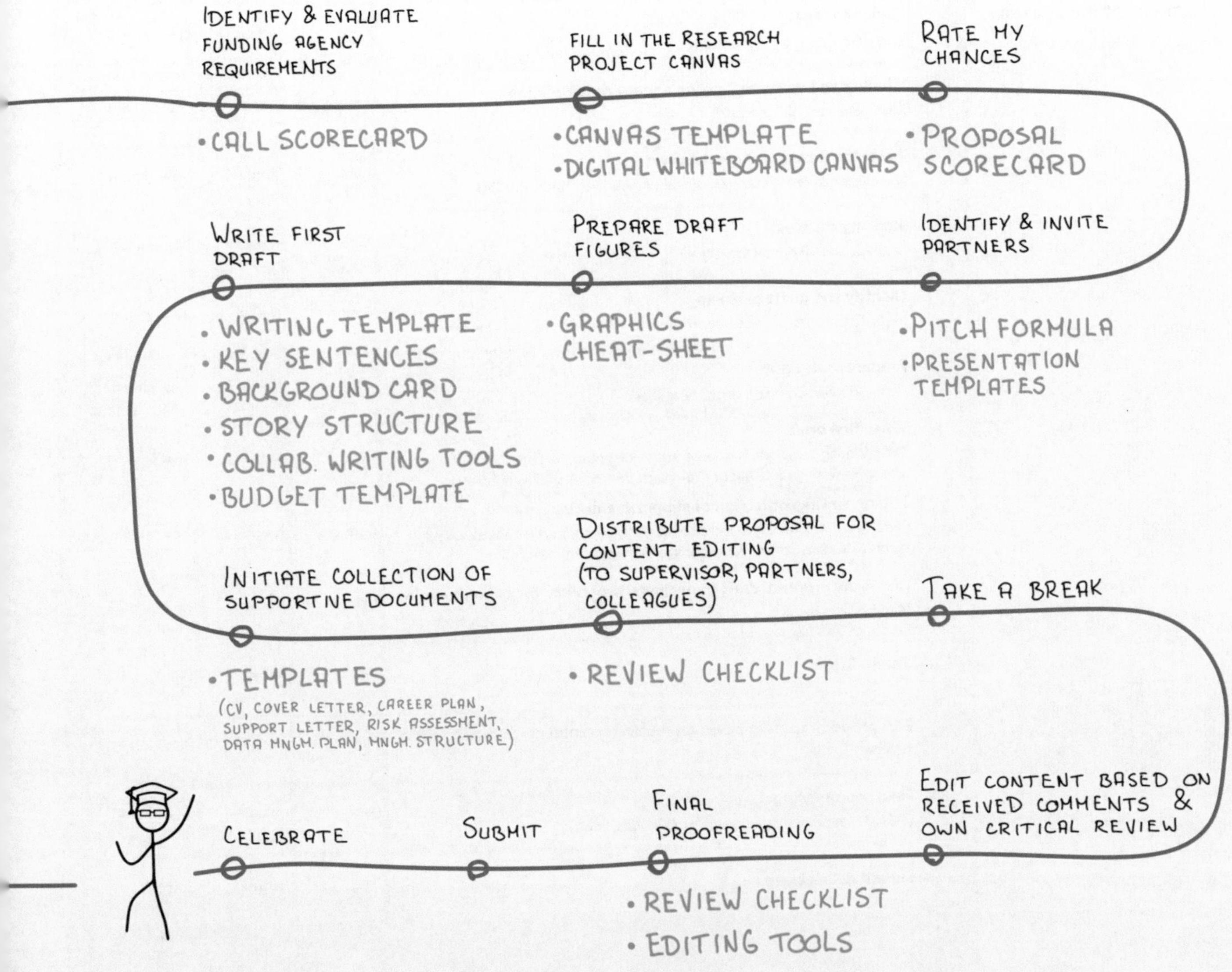

Identify & evaluate funding agency requirements
- Call scorecard

Fill in the research project canvas
- Canvas template
- Digital whiteboard canvas

Rate my chances
- Proposal scorecard

Write first draft
- Writing template
- Key sentences
- Background card
- Story structure
- Collab. writing tools
- Budget template

Prepare draft figures
- Graphics cheat-sheet

Identify & invite partners
- Pitch formula
- Presentation templates

Initiate collection of supportive documents
- Templates
  (CV, cover letter, career plan, support letter, risk assessment, data mngm. plan, mngm. structure)

Distribute proposal for content editing (to supervisor, partners, colleagues)
- Review checklist

Take a break

Edit content based on received comments & own critical review

Final proofreading
- Review checklist
- Editing tools

Submit

Celebrate

To aid with planning, you can use the **Research Proposal Writing Workflow** template.

Add and delete items in the template according to your own workflow and the requirements of the agency.

Research Proposal Writing Workflow

Project: `title`　　Designed by: `name`　　Date: `date`

	Due by	Done by	Status
Generate ideas (Aid: Idea Generator Worksheet)	Date	Name	How far is it?
Identify and evaluate funding agency requirements (Aid: Research Call Scorecard)	Date	Name	How far is it?
Fill in the Research Project Canvas (Aid: Research Project Canvas, Digital Whiteboard Project Canvas)	Date	Name	How far is it?
Rate my chances (Aid: Research Proposal Scorecard)	Date	Name	How far is it?
Identify and invite partners (Aids: Pitch Formula, Presentation templates, Research Project Canvas)	Date	Name	How far is it?
Prepare draft figures (Aids: Scientific Graphic Design cheat sheet)	Date	Name	How far is it?
Write first draft (Aids: Writing Template, Key Sentences, Background Card, Story Structure, Collaborative writing tools, Budget Template, Writing Workflow template)	Date	Name	How far is it?
Initiate writing/collection of supportive documents (Aids: templates for: CV, cover letter, career plan, support letter, risk assessment, data management plan, management structure description)	Date	Name	How far is it?
Distribute proposal draft to partners/supervisor for content editing (Aid: Review Checklist)	Date	Name	How far is it?
Take a break	Date	Name	How far is it?
Edit proposal content based on received comments and own critical review	Date	Name	How far is it?
Final proofreading (Aids: Review Checklist, language proofreading tools)	Date	Name	How far is it?
Submit & Celebrate	Date	Name	How far is it?

 **Peer Recognized** https://peerrecognized.com

Download the **Proposal Writing Workflow** template from https://peerrecognized.com/projectcanvas

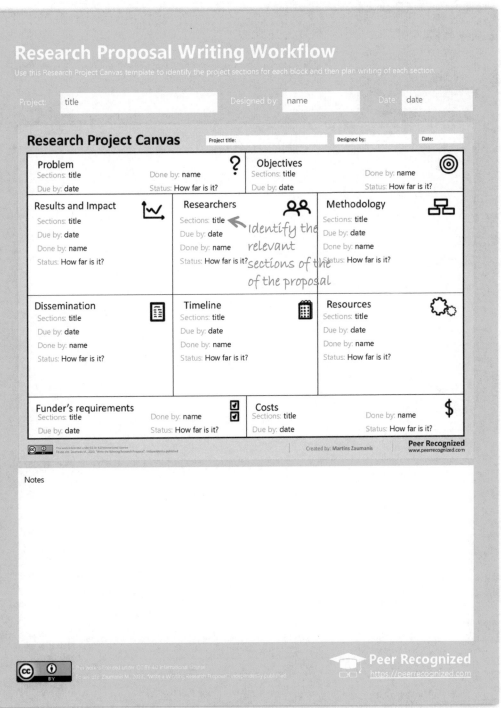

Research Proposal Writing Workflow

Use this Research Project Canvas template to identify the project sections for each block and then plan writing of each section.

Project: title   Designed by: name   Date: date

Research Project Canvas

Project title: Designed by: Date:

Problem ?
Sections: title   Done by: name
Due by: date   Status: How far is it?

Objectives ◎
Sections: title   Done by: name
Due by: date   Status: How far is it?

Results and Impact
Sections: title
Due by: date
Done by: name
Status: How far is it?

Researchers
Sections: title   ← *Identify the relevant sections of the of the proposal*
Due by: date
Done by: name
Status: How far is it?

Methodology
Sections: title
Due by: date
Done by: name
Status: How far is it?

Dissemination
Sections: title
Due by: date
Done by: name
Status: How far is it?

Timeline
Sections: title
Due by: date
Done by: name
Status: How far is it?

Resources
Sections: title
Due by: date
Done by: name
Status: How far is it?

Funder's requirements ☑ ☑
Sections: title   Done by: name
Due by: date   Status: How far is it?

Costs $
Sections: title   Done by: name
Due by: date   Status: How far is it?

Created by: **Martins Zaumanis**

Peer Recognized
www.peerrecognized.com

Notes

Peer Recognized
https://peerrecognized.com

When working in a team, you may want to use the second page of the template. Here you can assign who is responsible for describing each proposal section.

Coupled with the jointly-filled Project Canvas that holds the scientific description of the proposal, this template will help to ensure that everyone knows their tasks and is aware of the deadlines.

WHAT'S NEXT?

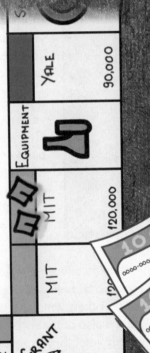
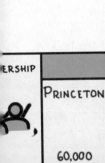

M ichael Jordan, a six-time NBA champion once said:

I've missed more than 9,000 shots in my career. I've lost al-most 300 games. Twenty-six times, I've been trusted to take the game-winning shot and missed. I've failed over and over and over again in my life. And that is why I succeed.

What Jordan says about shooting a basketball is just as true in research. A rejected proposal is simply part of the journey to an approved one.

First of all, every time you write a proposal you **polish your writing skills**. Practice matters, especially because, as discussed, proposal writing is different from paper writing.

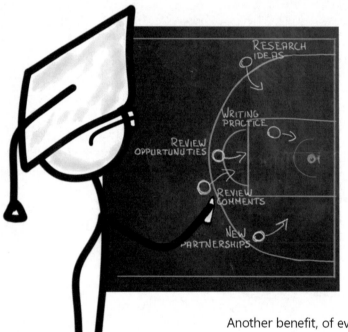

Secondly, good or bad, you will **get a review**. The reviewers need to substantiate their decisions and therefore rejected proposals typically contain more thorough comments than the accepted ones. This is your chance to learn and improve for the next time you submit, whether it is a revised version of the same one or an altogether new proposal.

If you write a proposal together with other scientists, you still keep the relationships that you built even after a rejection. Your **professional network** will expand and you will gather experience in collaborating with different people so that you will already know who to invite and who to avoid with the next proposal. Plus, the people you invite to join your projects are more likely to consider inviting you to join theirs.

Another benefit, of even a rejected proposal, is that you might get invited to **serve a proposal reviewer** yourself. This is a big deal since you will be able to learn how others write and thereby improve your own chances in the future. You will also probably be trained by the agency, so you will get to know exactly what they expect from proposals.

Some grant agencies allow potential reviewers to submit applications to serve as reviewers. By all means - do this.

Load the Dice

Michael Jordan played 1,251 games in his career so, admittedly, he had many chances to learn from his failures. Scientists don't have such a luxury.

In my experience, it is not possible to write more than a couple of good grant proposals per year. You either run out of time due to other obligations, or you run out of stamina since writing proposals takes a lot of mental energy.

Thankfully, a rejected proposal is not the only way to increase your prospects. The primary path to improving your odds of success is, well... to write better proposals. Since you are reading this book, I assume you realize the importance of this step and hopefully my advice will help you to improve further.

Besides writing better proposals, another way to increase your chances of getting funding is to polish your scientific profile. Reviewers of research proposals, unlike reviewers of most scientific journals, know the authors' names. In fact, the authors' qualification is usually one of the key criteria for rating a proposal.

No matter how good your proposal is, you can be sure that at least some of your competitors' proposals will be just as worthy of receiving funding as yours. Admittedly - luck will play a role.

Thankfully, unlike when rolling the dice, not everything depends on luck in proposal writing.

Improving your resume is like loading the dice in your favor. In the six books of the **Peer Recognized series**, I show you exactly how to do this (improve your resume, that is; you will have to look for other books if you want to learn how to cheat in Las Vegas).

Start now!

In Monopoly, the player who purchases the most valuable property first is usually the winner. Similarly, in academia, your chances of a successful career increase if you are an early achiever. The sooner you start building your academic profile, the greater your chances for acquiring funding, which in turn, will allow you to gather results, publish papers, and attend conferences that lead to citations, collaborations, and better prospects in the job market.

You have completed the fifth book of the Peer Recognized series. On the next page you will find a one-sentence summary of how the other books in the series will help you load the dice in your favor.

Peer Recognized Book Series

Book 1: Write an Impactful Research Paper

„A blueprint for confident academic writing that will accelerate your academic career."

https://peerrecognized.com/book1

Book 2: Research Data Visualization and Scientific Graphics

„The little push you need to get your papers accepted, your presentations remembered, and your research proposals approved."

https://peerrecognized.com/book2

Book 3: Scientific Presentation Skills

"The skills you need to ensure that your name is remembered from presentations and poster sessions."

https://peerrecognized.com/book3

Book 4: World Wide Scientist

"Turn your name into a brand on the biggest stage of them all."

https://peerrecognized.com/book4

Book 5: Write a Wiining Research Proposal

"Generate new research ideas and obtain funding to bring them to life ."

https://peerrecognized.com/book5

Book 6: Find Your Dream Job in Academia

"Build a name in science that makes academic employers fight to have you work for them."

https://peerrecognized.com/book6

Please rate this book on Amazon

It's the 15th of May, 2022. My wife thinks that I am at work and my boss thinks that I am on a vacation. In reality, I am sitting on a bench in a park writing this book.

Let me back up to explain how this happened.

I started writing the first book in the *Peer Recognized* series on the day my daughter, Mona, was born. In the following years, I would wake up to write before work and I absolutely loved the process.

Three years later, my second daughter, Hanna, was born. I planned to continue the writing routine for this very book that you are holding in your hands. To my absolute astonishment, it turned out that taking care of two girls takes more time than taking care of one. I had to squeeze writing sessions in during plane trips, commutes, and the occasional weekend. Six months into it, my progress was not great.

Then I found out that, starting this year, my employer increased the number of paternity leave days from 10 to 20. I did not know it and my wife is still not aware of it. So here I am, sitting in the park using my 10 extra days.

I would like to preemptively apologize to my daughter Hanna and my wife Liga for unknowingly giving me the extra days to write the book. I promise to take you on a great vacation once you find out about my deception.

★★★★★

Please leave a review for this book on Amazon. Good reviews might just help me justify to my family the decision to spend all those weekends and holidays writing. It would also give me the energy for continuing to help people like you with the Peer Recognized series books.

Martins Zaumanis

A big fat THANK YOU!

I would like to thank all the people who helped me finish this book, including Wino Wijnen, Cedric Vuye, Alvaro Garcia Hernandez, Nick Tyler, Ioannis Kousis, Martin Arraigada, Peter Richner, Pietro Lura, Christoph Röthlisberger, Alireza Fathollahi, Viktors Haritonovs, Mike Morrison, Laura Konstantaki, Lily Poulikakos, Sergio Copetti Callai, Nicholas Conzelmann, Nikolajs Toropovs, Rudy and Mahni Shayganfar, Jānis Tomaševskis, Abbas Solouki, Christina Makoundou, Mayara Lima, David Hernando, Maria Castellano, Michael Luber, Davide LoPresti, Diana and Ivars Erglļi, and Mukul Rathore. These people (and many others) offered me their ideas, commented on the book drafts, and pushed me to publish the books sooner. I am very thankful for that!

Like for all the previous books, Les Henderson deserves a big thank you for the patience in professionally editing the book. It's not an easy task, especially because I sometimes try to prove my non-native English is better than his very much native English.

My deepest gratitude goes to my daughters Hanna, Mona and my lovely wife Līga. I hope you can forgive me for spending our holidays writing this book.